'MILITARY MISREADINGS OF SHAKSPERE'

BY

MAJOR THOMAS SECCOMBE

FIRST PUBLISHED BY GEORGE ROUTLÉDGE & SONS, 1880

RE-INTRODUCED BY PAUL CORDLE, 2020

NINE ELMS BOOKS

Published in 2020 by Nine Elms Books Ltd

Unit 6B

Clapham North Arts Centre

26–32 Voltaire Road

London SW4 6DH

Email: info@nineelmsbooks.co.uk

www.nineelmsbooks.co.uk

ISBN: 978-1-910533-51-2

Thomas Seccombe's original book was first published in 1880 by George Routledge & Sons.

The illustration on Page 43 is reproduced by permission of the Bodleian Library, Oxford.

Design & Typography by September Design

Printed in India

CONTENTS

FOREWORD

This book is fun; it throws an amusing light on the British Army as the British Empire approached the apogee of its power.

Unsurprisingly, the British Army now looks very different in structure and style than it did in Seccombe's day. However, the lineage remains firmly embedded in today's regiments, not least because of the varied and sometimes peculiar traditions associated with their history.

These links with the great achievements and sometimes costly failures of the past create a resilience that is a particular mark of the British Army. To a large extent, the reforms put in place from the 1860s onwards were in response to clear failings in the existing systems. More recently they have been introduced in response to advances in technology, shifts in geopolitics, and financial and economic pressures. Many have been deeply resented and resisted by the Army and in some cases by the public. Perhaps 'twas ever thus'.

This short book should make a colourful addition to the home of anyone remotely interested in military history and Shakespeare; and I wish it success.

General Sir Jack Deverell KCB OBE DL

INTRODUCTION & ACKNOWLEDGEMENTS

Military Misreadings of Shakspere with its glorious misspelling was first published by George Routledge & Sons in 1880; it enjoyed great popularity with six editions being printed in 1880 and 1881. It seems that few copies have survived in good condition, hence the book is now being re-introduced in colour for the first time since its original publication. It is intended to give today's reader an amusing glimpse into the colourful world of the British Army of the late 19th century, as seen by an insider, and a quiet chuckle with William Shakespeare.

Seccombe's well observed, carefully drawn and humorous illustrations speak for themselves; they are of characters and situations in Queen Victoria's army with which he was familiar as an officer in the Royal Regiment of Artillery. He must have known Shakespeare's work well, choosing for each illustration a pithily appropriate quotation from the great Bard's plays; the combination of illustration and quotation is charming. Clearly with tongue in cheek Seccombe artfully added a disclaimer about his intentions.

Thomas Strong Seccombe, born in Calcutta on 24th February 1840, the son of Thomas Seccombe and his wife Caroline, was baptised at Fort William, Bengal on 22nd March 1840. Following officer training at the Royal Military Academy Woolwich he was commissioned into the Royal Artillery and saw service in Malta. He married Amelia Blanche Kennedy in St Helier, Jersey on 4th June 1867; he was gazetted Major in 1875 and retired from the Army in 1881 as a Lieutenant Colonel.

Seccombe created conventional images of people serving the Crown and of scenes of naval and military incident, he was, however, best known for his military sketches and caricatures; a collection of these was published as *Army and Navy Drolleries* by Frederick Warne in 1873 and 1876. On retirement he lived in Clapham, London and enjoyed success as an illustrator and author; he illustrated the acclaimed *Miss Kilmansegg and her Precious Leg* written by Thomas Hood (1799 – 1845) for which engravings were made by Edmund Evans (1826 – 1905). The date of his death is unclear; it is thought that he died in 1899.

Much has changed since Seccombe's time but, in spite of the reduction in numbers of our old and proud regiments, it is evident from campaigns and operations in the first decade of the 21st century that the pride and fighting spirit, the elan and swagger of the past continue just as strongly in the British Army of today albeit in less colourful uniforms. Officers and men draw on the legacy of their forebears as their regiments continue their centuries-old service to the Crown; it is hoped that this book will entertain them and give them good reason to celebrate what has gone before.

Enjoyment of Seccombe's artistry rests in the combination of illustration and quotation; this is the essence of the book. I have therefore felt free to make changes to the format of the original book which I think improve the reader's appreciation of his work. He arranged his images in no particular order, I have grouped them by type. I have included an 'extra' illustration unexpectedly found in one of the original editions but not in others. To add interest I have also included comments about each illustration and the outline history of identifiable regiments and connected Corps and thus provide the reader with pointers to the origins of some of the regiments and Corps in the British Army of the 21st century.

I acknowledge Thomas Seccombe for the originality of his well observed and beautifully executed work. I have drawn on various sources, notably on J.M. Brereton's *A Guide to the Regiments and Corps of the British Army* (The Bodley Head, 1985) and Allan Mallinson's *The Making of the British Army* (Bantam Books, 2011). I am indebted to the Revd (Colonel) Andrew Lloyd, Director of the Army Museum's Ogilby Trust for access to the Trust's list of succession of regiments and their changing titles.

I am indebted to Helen Gilio of the Bodleian Library for her patient help in providing the 'extra' illustration on page 43. I thank two former brother officers, Major General Sir Evelyn Webb-Carter for the use of his copy of Seccombe's original book and Joe Buxton for his research into the artist's life. I am also indebted to Lieutenant Colonel Ralph Griffin, Regimental Adjutant Household Cavalry and Stephanie Killingbeck-Turner, Assistant Curator of the Fusilier Museum, London for their answers to tiresome questions and to Christopher Joll, Regimental Historian Household Cavalry, for his scrutiny of the text and welcome suggestions. I thank General Sir Jack Deverell for most kindly writing a foreword.

Throughout the preparation of this short book Jan Kalinowski of September Design and Anthony Weldon of Nine Elms Books have been a source of sound guidance and enthusiastic help; without them this whole project would have come to nothing. I thank them.

Paul Cordle
June 2020.

of

by

Major Seccombe.

PRINTED IN COLOURS BY EDMUND EVANS.

LONDON
GEORGE ROUTLEDGE AND SONS
BROADWAY, LUDGATE HILL.
NEW YORK: 416 BROOME STREET.

ORIGINAL TITLE PAGE AND MAJOR SECCOMBE'S DISCLAIMER IN THE 1880 AND 1881 EDITIONS

"In submitting these Military Caricatures to the public, the artist, would disclaim all intention of reflecting upon the powers of equitation, etc, of any particular corps, the uniforms of regiments represented having been chosen solely for variety".

ILLUSTRATIONS & QUOTATIONS

> "This jarring discord of Nobility, this should'ring of each other in the court."
> HENRY VI., PART I. — ACT IV., SCENE 1.

LEVÉE

King Charles II adopted the French custom of levées in 1672; the British practice moved from a few favoured gentlemen attending the Monarch on rising to a formal reception later in the day. Until 1938 levées were held at St James's Palace at which only male officials, diplomats and officers of the Armed Forces were presented to the Sovereign; Court or military uniform was worn. The idea was that order and dignity would be maintained by the presence of the Body Guard; Seccombe saw it otherwise.

HER MAJESTY'S BODY GUARD OF THE HONOURABLE CORPS OF GENTLEMEN AT ARMS

King Henry VIII formed the 'Troop of Gentlemen' in 1509 to act as his mounted escort at home or abroad; it was composed of cadets of noble families. Called his 'Nearest Guard', it accompanied the King to France in 1513, was present at the Battle of the Spurs and at the Field of Cloth of Gold in 1520; in 1526 it became a dismounted body guard at Court carrying a long ceremonial axe which is still used today. It last acted as a royal bodyguard in battle during the Civil Wars 1642-49. It was known as the Honourable Band of Gentlemen Pensioners until 1834 when it acquired its present title. The uniform is that of a Dragoon Guards officer of the 1840s; the helmet has white swan feather plumes.

Her Majesty's Body Guard of the Honourable Corps of Gentlemen at Arms continues to provide a ceremonial bodyguard to The Queen on State occasions throughout the year.

IN THE LINE OF DUTY

A Member of the Body Guard chances his dignity in public near St James's Palace.

HER MAJESTY'S BODY GUARD OF THE HONOURABLE CORPS OF GENTLEMEN AT ARMS

From the earliest time Gentlemen at Arms have received countless honours and awards for gallant and meritorious service; amongst them twelve have been holders of the Victoria Cross, the United Kingdom's highest award for valour since it was instituted in 1856. The position of Captain of the Body Guard is a Government Post and, since 1945, has been held by the Government Chief Whip in the House of Lords.

GRENADIER GUARDS

In the background is a Private of the Grenadier Guards identified by his single buttons. King George V granted the rank of 'Guardsman' to private soldiers of all five regiments of Foot Guards in 1920.

King Charles II raised The King's Regiment of Guards whilst in exile in Bruges in 1656. Soon after his Restoration he raised a second regiment of Guards with the same name in London. In 1662, he brought the Bruges regiment to England and in 1665 combined the two regiments to become The First Regiment of Guards known as The First Guards, a title which it kept until 1815. It was then renamed The First or Grenadier Regiment of Foot Guards; this was in recognition of the decisive part it played at the Battle of Waterloo against the advancing columns of the Grenadiers of Napoleon's Old Guard, resplendent in their bearskin caps. The privilege of wearing the bearskin cap was also granted to the regiment and, for uniformity amongst Household Troops, this privilege was extended to the Coldstream and Scots Guards and, briefly, the three regiments of Household Cavalry in the early 1830s.

LEG-UP!

A Gunner (private soldier) in a Field Battery of the Royal Artillery appears to be well below the late 19th century national average height of 5 feet 5 inches for men. Gun horses stood between 15-16 hands at the withers (approx. 5ft – 5½ ft) and above this Gunner's ability to mount without help.

ROYAL REGIMENT OF ARTILLERY

Artillery (or ordnance) was first used in the English Army at the Battle of Crécy, 1346 but, until the early 18th century there was no permanent body of artillery. Ordnance, under the control of the Ordnance Office (later Board), was stored in the Tower of London and trains of artillery were formed when needed. In 1716 two companies of Field Artillery were raised at Woolwich by Royal Warrant of King George I. In 1793 the first two troops of Horse Artillery were raised and in due course fortress and coastal defence batteries were established in the United Kingdom and across the British Empire. By the middle of the 19th century the Royal Artillery was able to deploy twenty-nine batteries of horse artillery, seventy-three field batteries and eighty-eight garrison batteries.

> "And, after this; and then to breakfast with what appetite you have."
>
> HENRY VIII., — ACT III., SCENE 2.

ARTILLERY PRACTICE ON THE RANGE

An early start for Range Wardens off the coast, possibly at the School of Artillery ranges at Shoeburyness, Essex.

ROYAL REGIMENT OF ARTILLERY

Towards the end of the Victorian era the Royal Artillery was structured into three branches; the Royal Horse Artillery (RHA), the Royal Field Artillery (RFA), both horse drawn, and the Royal Garrison Artillery (RGA). In 1924, the RFA and RGA titles were dropped and batteries were reformed as the Royal Artillery; the Royal Horse Artillery retained its title. The Royal Artillery has been present in almost every British Army campaign since its inception; its motto is *Ubique* – everywhere.

CORPS OF ROYAL ENGINEERS

Ubique is also one of the mottoes of the Corps of Royal Engineers which also owes its origin to the Ordnance Office. From much earlier than the 18th century a body of men had been used in Royal Arsenals and fortifications; in 1716 a permanent officer corps of engineers was established with the title Corps of Engineers, the 'Royal' prefix was granted in 1787. A separate Corps of Royal Military Artificers was formed in 1787 consisting only of non-commissioned ranks with officers attached from the Corps of Engineers; in 1813 the 'Artificer' title was changed to Royal Sappers and Miners thus giving rise to the nickname 'Sappers' by which the Royal Engineers are familiarly known today. With the abolition of the Board of Ordnance in 1855, The Royal Artillery, the Royal Corps of Engineers and the Royal Sappers and Miners came directly under the control of the War Office.

SPORTING CHANCE

The Trooper's purpose is as clear as Seccombe shows him to be from 1st Life Guards by the red piping on his cross belt. The Regiment, amalgamated with the 2nd Life Guards in 1922, continues to use red piping today.

THE LIFE GUARDS

The Regiment was raised around 1658 by the exiled King Charles II from sixty mounted gentlemen in Bruges and was gradually formed into three Troops of Horse Guards. At the Restoration in 1660 these Troops returned to England with the King and escorted him to London. Later additions and a further restructuring in 1788 led to the forming of 1st and 2nd Regiments of Life Guards. The two regiments were amalgamated in 1922 and named The Life Guards. Various items of the Regiment's uniform and horse furniture are embellished with acorns and oak leaves; these recall the time when King Charles hid in an oak tree at Boscobel at the start of his six week escape to France following defeat at the Battle of Worcester in 1651. The King hid with a Major William Careless who later joined him in exile and was commissioned into The King's Regiment of Guards now the Grenadier Guards.

> "That what you cannot, as you would, achieve, you must perforce accomplish as you may."
>
> TITUS ANDRONICUS. — ACT II., SCENE 1.

FOLLOW MY LEADER

A 2nd Life Guards officer, identified by the dark blue piping on his cross belt, is brought down during manoeuvres. One wonders if the same fate awaits the second officer.

THE LIFE GUARDS

The Life Guards remained a horsed cavalry regiment until well into the 20th century. It may surprise the reader that, at the beginning of the Second World War, the Household Cavalry Composite Regiment , consisting of elements of The Life Guards and Royal Horse Guards (The Blues) was mobilised as a mounted regiment and was sent to the Middle East with its horses in early 1940; it was mechanised later that year.

Today the Household Cavalry continues its service in a composite form with The Life Guards and The Blues and Royals each forming part of both the operational Household Cavalry Regiment and the ceremonial Household Cavalry Mounted Regiment. The latter is based in Knightsbridge Barracks where, by and large, a regiment of the Household Cavalry has been since 1795.

"In peace, was never gentle lamb more mild."
RICHARD II. — ACT II., SCENE 1.

DOMESTIC DUTY

An Officer of The Blues, in full fig, trying hard to impress.

ROYAL HORSE GUARDS (THE BLUES)

The Regiment owes its origin to a Parliamentary regiment of horse raised in 1650; the restored King Charles II brought it into royal service as The Royal Regiment of Horse in 1661. It continued to wear a blue uniform, as it had before, but now the colour of the livery of its Colonel, the Earl of Oxford; they were nicknamed 'The Oxford Blues'. In 1750 the regiment was retitled the Royal Horse Guards Blue, a title it kept until 1819 when it was re-styled Royal Horse Guards (The Blues); it became part of the Household Cavalry in 1820 and until 1969 was commonly known as The Blues.

THE ROYAL DRAGOONS (1ST DRAGOONS)

The Royal Dragoons were raised as The Tangier Horse in 1661 by King Charles II. Besides their many Battle Honours, the Royals particularly distinguished themselves at the Battle of Waterloo when they captured the Eagle of the French 105th Regiment during the charge of the Union Brigade.

THE BLUES AND ROYALS (ROYAL HORSE GUARDS & 1ST DRAGOONS)

These two illustrious regiments were amalgamated in 1969. The regiment forms part of the operational Household Cavalry Regiment and the Household Cavalry Mounted Regiment sharing both roles with The Life Guards. A gold Eagle, recalling the Royals' Waterloo prize, is still worn as a badge on the left arm of the Regiment's uniform.

EXTENSION MOTIONS

This is Seccombe's intriguing title for Physical Training in a regiment of Dragoons, identified by their scarlet stable jackets, possibly The Royal Dragoons or King's Dragoon Guards both of which he included in his book. The reader can but wonder how this strenuous activity was managed with spurs.

ROYAL ARMY PHYSICAL TRAINING CORPS

British public opinion about the conduct of the Crimean War and the poor conditions endured by the ordinary soldier, particularly in the infantry, gave rise to various enquiries. These resulted in a widespread tranche of reforms which led to improvements in the provision of better food, health and welfare support, sport and education. The Army Gymnastic Staff was founded in 1860 to improve soldiers' health and physical resilience; physical training with competitions to stimulate interest were introduced. Further improvements in soldiers' health and fitness were made following the introduction of the Army Manual of Physical Training in 1908. The Army Gymnastic Staff was renamed the Army Physical Training Corps in 1918 and granted the 'Royal' prefix in 2010.

HOT PURSUIT

The collar badges of rank lead one to think that this is the Commanding Officer of the Royal Dragoons (1st Dragoons); if so, this image would have given much amusement to the regiment. In hot pursuit are troopers of the 12th Lancers wearing the blue uniform of a Light Cavalry regiment with red facings and the distinctive Chapka or Czapka helmet of Polish design worn by Lancers.

THE ROYAL DRAGOONS (1ST DRAGOONS)

Raised in 1661, The Tangier Horse formed the cavalry element of the garrison in the city given to King Charles II as part of Catherine of Braganza's dowry. It was one of a very few regiments to have been awarded the British Army's first Battle Honour 'Tangier' distinguished by the dates 1662 – 80.

When brought back to England, the Regiment was restyled as the King's Own Royal Regiment of Dragoons; by 1924 it was known as 1st The Royal Dragoons. In 1969, the regiment was amalgamated with The Royal Horse Guards (The Blues) to form The Blues and Royals (Royal Horse Guards and 1st Dragoons).

12TH ROYAL LANCERS (PRINCE OF WALES'S)

Raised in 1715 as a regiment of Dragoons, restyled in 1768 as 12th (or The Prince of Wales's) Regiment of (Light) Dragoons, the Regiment became a regiment of lancers in 1816. See page 32.

> "What power is it, which mounts my love so high?"
>
> ALL'S WELL THAT ENDS WELL. — ACT I., SCENE 1.

FLIGHT OF FANCY

The number '2' can just be seen above KDG on the saddle roll and one might suppose that this is 2 Squadron Leader of the King's Dragoon Guards in which scarlet tunics were worn.

KING'S DRAGOON GUARDS

The regiment was raised, in response to the Monmouth Rebellion, in 1685 as The Queen's Regiment of Horse and ranked as the 2nd Horse after 1st Dragoons. In 1714 it was restyled as The King's Own Regiment of Horse and in 1746 as the 1st (or The King's) Regiment of Dragoon Guards. In 1896, on his appointment as Colonel, Emperor Franz Joseph of Austria granted the Regiment the right to wear the Austrian double-headed eagle as its badge. With Austria being allied to Germany this was discontinued during the First World War; wearing of the badge was resumed in 1937 and continues today in its successor regiment the 1st The Queen's Royal Dragoons, the senior cavalry regiment of the line. The Radetzky March, also owed to Emperor Franz Joseph, continues as the regimental march.

> "I do not without danger walk these streets."
>
> TWELFTH NIGHT., — ACT III., SCENE 3.

TRIP HAZARD

A Cornet (2nd Lieutenant) of the 13th Hussars facing a challenge which is not unfamiliar today for those wearing mounted dress with sword. In this case the officer has also to contend with his sabretache, the flat dispatch case hanging from the sword belt.

13TH HUSSARS

Raised in 1715 as a regiment of Dragoons it had, by 1783, become 13th Regiment of (Light) Dragoons; it became the 13th Hussars in 1862. The regiment had a proud record of service earned throughout the Peninsular War and at Waterloo; it was during the Crimean War that it acquired immortal fame by being part of The Light Brigade during its ill-fated charge at the Battle of Balaclava.

> "He that commends me to mine own content, commends me
> to the thing I cannot get."
>
> COMEDY OF ERRORS. — ACT I., SCENE 2.

TOOTHACHE

A Hussar officer in camp troubled by toothache and challenged by foul weather. Seccombe's eye for detail includes the brass corner of the campaign chest, the washing bowl and toothbrush, the camp bath and sponge.

No provision for dental care was made in the British Army in Seccombe's time nor until the First World War when a few Dental Officers served in the Royal Army Medical Corps. It was not until 1921 that the Army Dental Corps was formed; the 'Royal' prefix was granted in 1946.

HUSSAR REGIMENTS

During the 17th and early 18th centuries British cavalry consisted almost entirely of regiments of Dragoons Guards and of the lighter horsed Dragoons; both were equipped to fight as mounted infantry as much as cavalry. During the second half of the 18th century and particularly during the Napoleonic wars the need for faster light cavalry emerged; several regiments of dragoons were restyled and equipped as Hussars and Lancers.

> "Prepared I was not for such a business; therefore am I found
> so much unsettled."

ALL'S WELL THAT ENDS WELL. — ACT II., SCENE 5.

OFFICERS' EQUITATION

Seccombe does not help the reader with any regimental detail except that officers of this Hussar regiment wear the blue uniform of the Light Cavalry.

BRITISH CAVALRY IN THE MID-19TH CENTURY.

British cavalry in the mid-19th century is better known for its courage and dash than for its effectiveness; unimaginative and poor leadership reduced its potential on the battlefield. Its uniforms were tight and impractical for the cut and thrust of battle and the design of saddlery and horse furniture needed improvement. These weaknesses were pointed out by Captain LE Nolan (1818-1854) of the 15th Light Dragoons (Hussars), best known for his part as a 'galloper' in delivering the order from Lord Raglan to Lord Lucan for The Light Brigade to charge at the Battle of Balaclava. Many of Nolan's recommendations were adopted after his death towards the end of the century.

Nolan wrote "The qualities requisite in a cavalry leader are a good eye for country and a quick one for the enemy's movements, great energy, courageous decision, and rapid execution." He added more inclusively with all ranks in mind "that individual prowess, skill in single combat, good horsemanship, and sharp swords, render all cavalry formidable... and that speed and endurance are qualities to be highly prized in the horseman."

"Our Captain hath in every figure skill."

TIMON OF ATHENS. — ACT V., SCENE 4.

SHARP PRACTICE

Even today spurs continue to make dancing a precarious business but this 11th Hussar officer appears to be managing well enough. To the left, with exquisite detail, Seccombe included an officer from another Hussar regiment inviting a lady to dance as he presents his dance card. In the background an officer from an infantry regiment dances unencumbered by spurs.

11TH HUSSARS (PRINCE ALBERT'S OWN)

The Regiment was raised in 1715 as a regiment of dragoons and by 1751 was numbered the 11th Regiment of Dragoons, it became a light cavalry regiment in 1783. It was designated as a regiment of Hussars in 1840 and was restyled as the 11th (Prince Albert's Own) Hussars.

The 11th Hussars were unique among cavalry regiments in wearing crimson overalls, a distinction authorised by Queen Victoria in 1840; their nickname became 'The Cherrypickers'. During the Crimean War the Regiment gained immortal fame by taking part in the Charge of The Light Brigade at the Battle of Balaclava. Its descendant regiment The King's Royal Hussars continues to wear crimson overalls. The 11th Hussars and the 9th/12th Lancers were the first cavalry regiments in the British Army to be mechanised, converting to armoured cars in 1928.

"My Lord, I scarce have leisure to salute you."

TROILUS AND CRESSIDA. — ACT IV., SCENE 2.

TROT PAST

A hapless Squadron Leader of the 12th Lancers lets his immaculate squadron down as it trots past an inspecting General. The Regiment wears the blue uniform of a Light Cavalry regiment with red facings and the distinctive Chapka or Czapka helmet of Polish design. In true style Seccombe picks out the details of The Prince of Wales's feathers on the sabretache and shabraque.

The General is accompanied by a German officer (eagles on Imperial German badges were single headed whilst on Russian and Austrian imperial badges eagles were double-headed); the Commanding Officer or Colonel of the Regiment waves his sword in incandescent rage. Beyond the inspecting officers are various officers, amongst them an officer from the Royal Navy, the Foot Guards, the RHA or Hussars and one with a distinctly French or Belgian moustache and cap.

12TH LANCERS (PRINCE OF WALES'S)

The Regiment was raised in 1715 as a regiment of Dragoons. In 1768 it was titled 12th (or The Prince of Wales's) Regiment of (Light) Dragoons and in 1816 the 12th (or The Prince of Wales's) Regiment of Lancers, it being one of the first three British cavalry regiments to be converted to Lancers following lessons learned at the Battle of Waterloo. The 12th Lancers and the 11th Hussars were the first cavalry regiments in the British Army to be mechanised, converting to armoured cars in 1928. In 1960 the 12th Royal Lancers (Prince of Wales's) was amalgamated with the 9th Queen's Royal Lancers to form the 9th/12th Royal Lancers (Prince of Wales's); see Appendix 3 for subsequent amalgamations.

"I looked upon her with a soldier's eye, that liked,
but had a rougher task in hand."

MUCH ADO ABOUT NOTHING. — ACT I., SCENE 1.

AN UNPROMISING START

The situation conjured up in this delightful image may resonate with many a reader. A Major in the 17th Lancers has a duty to perform; the 13th Hussar officer in the background has an easier time of it.

17TH LANCERS (DUKE OF CAMBRIDGE'S OWN)

The Regiment was raised in 1759 as the 18th Regiment of (Light) Dragoons; it was later renumbered 17th and in 1823 acquired the role of lancers. As the 17th (Light) Dragoons (Lancers) it took part in the major battles of the Crimean war and charged with The Light Brigade at the Battle of Balaclava thus acquiring immortal fame. Its motto *Or Glory*.

The regiment was amalgamated with the 21st Lancers (Empress of India's) in 1922 to become the 17th/21st Lancers. The new regiment with its distinctive badge of 'Skull and Cross Bones' and motto *Or Glory* was known by the nickname 'The Death or Glory Boys'.

> "Where every horse bears his commanding rein, and may direct
> his course as please himself."
>
> RICHARD III. — ACT II., SCENE 2.

FENCIBLES

The quotation above says it all. Perhaps, in spite of his disclaimer, Seccombe felt it would have been going too far to identify any particular Yeomanry cavalry regiment with this chaos. This may account for his choice of an unusual blue-grey uniform and the simple '1YC' on the roll behind the saddle.

YEOMANRY CAVALRY

Troops of Yeomanry cavalry were formed in many counties in the 1790s to help defend the country against the threat of a French invasion; generically they were known as 'Fencibles' from 'defencible'. After 1815 and during the early part of the 19th century their role was to support the Civil Power; as local police constabularies developed the Fencibles' role became redundant, many troops were disbanded whilst others were brought together to form regiments. In 1876 their role was fixed as light cavalry for home service only; this changed with the Boer War when volunteers from all yeomanry regiments were called for overseas service with the Imperial Yeomanry.

From 1901 all yeomanry regiments were restyled 'Imperial Yeomanry', in 1908 they were brought into The Territorial Force and later fought in all theatres during the First and Second World Wars in a variety of roles. Four yeomanry regiments remain in the British Army today proudly playing an essential part in the country's defence; the Royal Yeomanry, the Royal Wessex Yeomanry, the Queen's Own Yeomanry, the Scottish and North Irish Yeomanry.

MUSICAL DISCORD

The unfortunate Yeomanry trooper is nowhere to be seen as his charger scatters the Band of the Grenadier Guards. The regiment is not identifiable other than by 'BYC' on the saddle roll; this might denote 'B' Squadron or possibly Berkshire, Bedfordshire or Buckinghamshire all of which had a yeomanry regiment.

BAND OF THE GRENADIER GUARDS

The Grenadier Guards were raised by King Charles II in 1656 as The King's Regiment of Guards. Music in the Regiment owes its origin to 1664 when a musician was engaged to train a flute player in each of its twenty-four companies. In 1685, the King authorised the maintenance of twelve hautbois and from that time the range of music was gradually extended with the introduction of new instruments; at its largest the Band had sixty musicians. Until well into the 20th century black mourning bands, in memory of King Charles II, were worked into each arm of the tunic worn by the Time Beater (bass drummer); unusually Seccombe did not pick up on this detail and the mourning bands are not included on the tunic of the prostrate musician.

George Frederick Handel composed the slow march 'Scipio' and presented it to the Regiment before including it in his opera of that name. Three other pieces of music associated with the Grenadier Guards are the slow 'The Duke of York's March', the quick or slow 'The Grenadier's March' and the traditional quick march 'The British Grenadiers'. This was widely used by grenadier companies throughout the British Army during the 18th century and, whilst not exclusive to the Grenadier Guards, this famous march tune defines the Regiment.

Today all Army musicians are part of The Corps of Army Music which was formed in 1994.

THE KIDDIES

This Scots Guards Ensign (2nd Lieutenant) faces the same height challenge that some officers in the Foot Guards face today. Seccombe properly includes the young officer's thin moustache; to have one was a requirement for all ranks of the British Army under Queen's and King's Regulations until withdrawn in 1916; officers in the Brigade of Guards were expected to have them up to the Second World War, thereafter the custom became less common.

SCOTS GUARDS

The Regiment's origin goes back to 1642 when raised by King Charles I for service in Ireland. It returned to Scotland, fought for King Charles II at the Battle of Worcester in 1651 and was then disbanded by Oliver Cromwell; it was re-formed in 1662 by Royal Warrant of King Charles II. In 1686 the Regiment was brought into the English establishment, named Scotch or Scotts Guards, and took precedence as the third regiment of Foot Guards after The First Guards and The Coldstream Guards; this gave rise to its nickname 'The Kiddies'. From 1831 – 1877 the Regiment was named Scots Fusilier Guards, the only regiment in the British Army to have been designated 'Fusilier Guards'; Queen Victoria conferred the present title of Scots Guards in 1877.

Due to its precedence in the Foot Guards the Regiment wears its buttons in threes and has no plume in its bearskin cap; the reason for this was that, during the 19th century, when it stood in line between the Grenadiers on the Right and the Coldstream on the Left there was no need for any feature by which to distinguish it. The Grenadiers wear white plumes on the left of their bearskins and the Coldstream wear red plumes on the right of their bearskins.

"Blame not this haste of mine."

TWELFTH NIGHT. — ACT IV., SCENE 3.

FORCE MAJEURE

This splendid bull has all before it! The men of The Royal Fusiliers wear the Valise Pattern equipment issued in 1871.

THE ROYAL FUSILIERS (CITY OF LONDON REGIMENT)

Raised in the Tower of London by King James II in 1685, The Royal Regiment of Fuzileers' (sic) primary role was to protect the ordnance stored in the Tower and escort the Train of Artillery on operations; thus it was also known as The Ordnance Regiment. Its first Colonel, Lord Dartmouth, was Master General of Ordnance. The Regiment was armed with a fusil, a flintlock weapon which avoided using, near gunpowder, the burning fuses of matchlocks, the older type of weapon used in the infantry.

The Royal Fusiliers, as other Fusilier regiments, wore bearskin caps, a custom which originated in the headdress of their grenadier companies in the 18th century. The Regiment recruited exclusively from the City of London; during the First World War it fielded an impressive total of forty-six battalions.

In 1968 The Royal Northumberland Fusiliers (5th), The Royal Warwickshire Fusiliers (6th), The Royal Fusiliers (7th) and The Lancashire Fusiliers (20th) were amalgamated to form The Royal Regiment of Fusiliers; its Regimental Headquarters is at the Tower of London.

Note: This is the 'extra' illustration which came to light during research for the book; it was on the front cover of one of the original 1880/1881 editions and is damaged. It is included by permission of the Bodleian Libraries, University of Oxford (Mal. L. 46, Front Cover).

> "Oh Hamlet, what a falling off was there."
> HAMLET. — ACT I., SCENE 5.

THIN RED LINE

It is difficult to say to which regiment Seccombe intended this officer and the men on page 47 to belong. The combination of Government tartan, facings and other details of uniform might lead some readers to select the Seaforth Highlanders, others to select either the 91st (Princess Louise's) Argyllshire Highlanders or the 93rd Sutherland Highlanders or indeed their successor regiment, The Argyll and Sutherland Highlanders (Princess Louise's) (91st and 93rd) formed by their amalgamation in 1881.

The 93rd gained immortal fame as the 'Thin Red Line' when it stood its ground in the face of Russian cavalry charges during the Crimean War at the Battle of Balaclava; it was the only regiment in the British Army to be awarded the Battle Honour 'Balaclava'. The amalgamated regiment showed similar tenacity and courage in Aden in 1967 when at night, against the odds but with a piper playing, it entered the terrorist occupied city of Crater.

"And my appointments have in them in a need, greater than shows itself at the first view, to you that know them not."

ALL'S WELL THAT ENDS WELL. — ACT II., SCENE 5.

PRICKLY BUSINESS

Since the Union of England and Scotland in 1707 the Scots have given generously of their men; their proud regiments have fought across the globe in almost every campaign of the British Army. The oldest of Scotland's regiments, The Royal Scots (The Royal Regiment) was first raised by King Charles I in 1633; in 1661, soon after his Restoration, King Charles II brought it back from foreign service into royal service as the 1st Regiment of Foot under the Colonelcy of the Earl of Dumbarton. Until amalgamation in 2006, the regiment considered itself so old that it adopted the sobriquet of 'Pontius Pilate's Bodyguard'.

SCOTLAND THE BRAVE

Seccombe would have been familiar with all Scottish regiments; they are listed below with their antecedent regiments' number in the line and earliest date of establishment in royal service.

The Royal Scots (1st/1661), The Royal Scots Fusiliers (21st/1678), The Highland Light Infantry (71st & 74th/1777), The King's Own Scottish Borderers (25th/1689), The Cameronians (26th & 90th/1689), The Black Watch (42nd & 73rd/1739), The Seaforth Highlanders (72nd, 78th & 79th/1778), The Gordon Highlanders (75th & 92nd/1787), The Argyll and Sutherland Highlanders (91st & 93rd/1794). Several of these regiments were successively disbanded or amalgamated during the last half of the 20th century and are now part of the multi-battalion Royal Regiment of Scotland in 2006.

In recognition of The Royal Scots' seniority, The Royal Regiment of Scotland now takes precedence over all other infantry regiments of the line. Officers and men of the regiment wear the Government A1 tartan whilst the Band and Pipes & Drums wear the tartans and headdress of their antecedent regiments thus maintaining the colourful traditions of their past.

"Content you, gentlemen; I'll compound this strife."

TAMING OF THE SHREW. — ACT II., SCENE 1.

AUTUMN MANOEUVRES – THE UMPIRE

In Seccombe's time, and even today at lower levels, an umpire was relied on to settle ticklish arguments during training. The variety of uniforms and the obvious heat of argument between the protagonists makes this illustration a delight. The inclusion of the unlimbered RHA gun and its men on the skyline, perhaps in earshot of the mêlée, sets a theatrical tone to this conversation piece.

Mounted to the extreme left is a RHA officer, perhaps the gun crew's Troop or Battery commander, making his point to a stuffy Hussar officer; to the left of centre is an officer of the 3rd Dragoon Guards appealing for sense from an officer in The King's Royal Rifle Corps (60th Rifles), beyond the umpire, helped it appears by a monocled Coldstream Guards officer in bearskin cap. Two line regiment officers, one in the foreground and the other beyond the Umpire's horse, are wearing the out-of-date Crimean War style cap, albeit shortened as per Continental fashion. To the right are two line regiment officers wearing the newly introduced spiked Home Service helmet and a Highland officer with whom one is about to come to blows. The Umpire, in the undress uniform of the General Staff, and smiling benignly, raises his hand for quiet.

3rd Dragoon Guards (Prince of Wales's), raised in 1685, was amalgamated in 1922 with the Carabiniers (6th Dragoon Guards) to form the 3rd/6th Dragoon Guards. Its title was changed to the 3rd Carabiniers (Prince of Wales's Dragoon Guards) in 1928. *Coldstream Guards*, raised in 1650 as a Parliamentary regiment during the Civil War, was brought into royal service by the restored King Charles II's service in 1661 with precedence below The First Guards. *The King's Royal Rifle Corps (60th)*, raised in North America in 1755 as The Royal American Regiment of Foot, was restyled in 1881 as The King's Royal Rifle Corps (KRRC). Following a succession of name changes and amalgamations in 1958 and 1960 The Royal Green Jackets emerged composed of The Oxfordshire and Buckinghamshire Light Infantry (43rd and 52nd), the KRRC and The Rifle Brigade.

> "Thou art a soldier, therefore seldom rich."
>
> TIMON OF ATHENS. — ACT I., SCENE 2.

CRITICAL INTERVIEW

A line regiment officer in undress jacket makes his case. At some point in the proceedings he would have also needed the permission of his commanding officer to marry; if under the age of 25 or otherwise deemed too early in his career, permission would not have been given.

MARRIAGE IN THE VICTORIAN ARMY

Officers were encouraged to marry and to settle down at an appropriate age and thus play a paternal role in the family of a regiment; their wives were expected to act in a maternal capacity and deal with welfare matters.

Marriage amongst other ranks was discouraged; permission to marry was given to six men in a hundred. Their wives were taken onto the strength of the regiment and some provision made for them. About nine men out of a hundred married without permission and no provision was made for their wives or families. A few 'on strength' wives, chosen by ballot, accompanied their husbands overseas; the few who went to the Crimean War proved themselves of great value to the men, tending the wounded, mending clothing and cooking.

> *"My spirit can no longer bear these harms."*
> HENRY VI., PART I. — ACT IV., SCENE 7.

SPIRITED AFFAIR

A bachelor officer surprises a servant on returning unexpectedly to his room; it was ever thus. It is difficult to work out who Seccombe imagined the servant to be as he is neither in uniform (a soldier servant) nor in mess livery.

DISCIPLINE IN THE VICTORIAN ARMY

A soldier's life in the Victorian army during peacetime was harsh and often tedious particularly when overseas; alcohol, whilst providing temporary relief from boredom, often gave rise to drunkenness, insubordination and fighting. Whilst minor infringements in discipline led to extra duties, punishment parades and loss of privileges, a commanding officer, for more serious offences, could reduce a non-commissioned officer to the ranks and sentence men to imprisonment and flogging. A court martial had greater powers and could pass more severe sentences of imprisonment, flogging, branding and discharge. By 1846 flogging was restricted to 50 lashes; it was gradually phased out in Home Garrisons but continued to be used overseas until 1881. Field Punishment (No 1) for very serious offences was introduced in 1881 following the abolition of flogging and remained in place until 1923.

"Your several suits have been considered and debated on."

HENRY VI., PART I. — ACT V., SCENE 1.

CLOTHING INSPECTION

The initial issue of uniforms to new recruits at their regimental depot was a big moment; a passable first fit depended on the eye of the clothing storeman. These men, including the member of staff with ledger, are wearing the Glengarry cap issued as undress headdress between 1868 and 1897. The officer wears an undress jacket and forage cap.

REGIMENTAL DEPOTS

Regimental depots were staffed by a company from each of a regiment's two regular battalions. The Depot Company trained its recruits, sent drafts of new soldiers to its parent battalion, stationed either at home or overseas, and in time of war processed reservists returning to the Colours and sent them to the battalion most in need of reinforcement.

"If I know how, or which way, to order these affairs, thus thrust disorderly into my hands, never believe me."

RICHARD II. — ACT II., SCENE 2.

PUZZLED

This is probably a young recruit (no moustache) during initial training at his regimental depot. Seccombe makes the most of this puzzling moment; young recruits in the Army today can be similarly baffled by newly issued items of equipment. One can just identity the soldier's rifle as a Martini-Henry by the lever under the wrist of the rifle stock.

MARTINI-HENRY RIFLE

This rifle was adopted as the standard infantry weapon in 1871 and was in service for 47 years; variants were made as carbines for Gunner and Cavalry regiments. It had a lever operated falling block action from which a rate of fire of 12 rounds a minute could be achieved. Although at its most effective at ranges up to 400 yards, it was also used for long range dropping fire volleys up to 1900 yards, its maximum range, to disrupt enemy massing or denying them the use of ground. Its .577/450 calibre round, manufactured with a metal casing, delivered severe wounds particularly at shorter ranges before its velocity reduced.

"But this is mere digression from my purpose."

HENRY IV., PART II. — ACT IV., SCENE 1.

IN THE LINE OF FIRE

Musketry Practice for a Volunteer Rifle Corps was an essential part of the annual training cycle and upon which its efficiency was judged. It appears that this Corps' shooting was worse than erratic resulting in the farmer claiming compensation for livestock shot. Part V of the Volunteer Act 1863 allowed for the acquisition of land to be used as rifle ranges and gave Justices of the Peace powers to close rights of way close to ranges; one wonders why this range was sited so close to a farmhouse and how often the farmer made such claims.

❖

VOLUNTEER RIFLE CORPS

From 1859, the raising of a Volunteers Rifle Corps was authorised by county Lord Lieutenants from whom officers received their commissions. Corps, with an intended establishment of 100 men under the command of a Captain, chose their own style of uniform, often grey.

By the provisions of the Regulation of the Forces Act 1871, jurisdiction of the Volunteer Force was placed under the Secretary of State for War and Corps were formed into battalions which became increasingly integrated with regular regiments and adopted their uniforms. Following the Haldane Reforms and the Territorial & Reserve Forces Act 1907 volunteer, militia and yeomanry regiments were absorbed into The Territorial Force.

In 1859 The National Rifle Association was set up to encourage sound marksmanship in Volunteer Rifle Corps and throughout the Queen's Dominions; its inaugural rifle meeting was held at the ranges on Wimbledon Common in 1860. Queen Victoria fired the first round by pulling a silk cord attached to the trigger of a rifle set in a metal rest; the winner was Mr Edward Ross of 7th North Yorkshire Volunteers. The ranges were moved to Bisley in 1890.

"But this exceeding posting, day and night, must wear your spirits low."

ALL'S WELL THAT ENDS WELL. — ACT V., SCENE 1.

STAFF WORK

An officer on the General Staff, perhaps the Brigade Major at Brigade Headquarters attended by Other Ranks from several regiments.

THE STAFF COLLEGE

The function of staff training in the British Army was started at The Royal Military College at High Wycombe in 1799; in 1802 it was recognised as the Senior Department of the College. In 1813 the Senior Department moved temporarily to Farnham and then rejoined The Royal Military College which had since moved to Sandhurst. Renamed The Staff College it was established as a separate entity in 1858; students had to pay to attend the two year course. The Staff College moved to a separate site at Camberley in 1870 where it remained until 1997.

"And I myself know well, how troublesome it sat upon my head."

HENRY IV., PART II. — ACT IV., SCENE 4.

TROUBLESOME GUST

With his grey hair and uniform this is, possibly, a Lieutenant General being troubled by the strong wind. His soldier servant perhaps, in the distance, is trying to rescue his master's belongings whilst, fancifully, Seccombe has added a flying drummer to emphasise how unpleasant the weather is.

THE STAFF

Although necessary to have staff officers trained for the serious business of managing large formations of troops it was felt, during the latter part of 19th century, that regimental duty was more honourable than appointment to the Staff. Some Commanding Officers were known to discourage attendance by their officers and Generals might appoint protegées to their staff instead of formally trained staff officers. The importance of staff training became apparent during the Second Boer War; in 1914 the British Expeditionary Force went to France with a well established staff structure at all levels of command.

ANNUAL INSPECTION

A line regiment formed up for inspection, in which, except for the tremulous young officer, Seccombe has been careful to give everyone a moustache; to have one was a requirement for all ranks under Queen's and King's Regulations from soon after the Crimean War until October 1916 when the regulation was withdrawn. This regiment wears the Home Service helmet, introduced in 1878, made of cloth-covered cork and topped with a spike reflecting similar Continental fashions. Soldiers are wearing the 1871 Valise Pattern equipment, their rifles are almost certainly the Martini-Henry.

INFANTRY OF THE LINE

Other than in rifle regiments, line regiments wore scarlet tunics with their own distinctive coloured facings, in this case green, regimental badges and other embellishments peculiar to their history, for example the 'flash' worn by The Royal Welch Fusiliers. This consisted of black ribbons of about 7 inches in length hanging down from under the collar on the back of the uniform jacket. The regiment, whilst on foreign service, was the last regiment to wear the powdered pigtail, or queue, and the flash represented the strip of material used to protect the uniform from the powder. Another example, amongst many, is the 'leaved acorn' worn by The Cheshire Regiment (22nd); this was to commemorate the action of a detachment of the 22nd which saved King George II from capture at the Battle of Dettingen in 1743. The King, on giving them a twig plucked from an oak tree, is said to have expressed his wish that it should be worn by the Regiment in memory of their gallant conduct. This was the last occasion on which a British Monarch led the Army in battle.

RUMBLED

As at kit inspections today, soldiers curl up in laughter at their comrade's discomfort, regimental officers look on askance whilst the General fulminates. The regimental officer in mounted order of dress behind the General, perhaps the Commanding Officer, appears unmoved. It is of note that Seccombe does not include any rifles, a soldier's most intimate piece of equipment, which were at times kept in barrack rooms.

INFANTRY SKILL AT ARMS

The tolerance of discomfort, marching long distances, musketry and bayonet fighting were and remain the stock in trade of British infantrymen; it is they who bear the brunt of war. Their musket or rifle was and remains their 'wife', courage, good humour, resilience and comradeship are their 'brothers', pride of regiment their 'lodestone'. These attributes and their skill at arms, seasoned with sheer 'bloody mindedness' in a tight corner, have given them a fighting reputation second to none.

THE SMALL ARMS SCHOOL CORPS

The introduction in 1851 of the Minié rifle required infantrymen to be more competent in skill at arms. In 1854, this small highly effective and greatly respected Corps was raised as the Corps of Instructors of Musketry at the newly established School of Musketry in Hythe which in 1919 was restyled as the Small Arms School. In due course, and separately, the Machine Gun School was formed at Seaford and later moved to Netheravon; in 1923 the two schools were re-designated the Corps of Small Arms and Machine Gun Schools. In 1929 they were amalgamated, whilst remaining in their separate locations, and the instructors became part of the Small Arms School Corps. Hythe was closed in 1969.

AUTHOR'S NOTE

A reader, uninitiated in the mysteries
of British Army affairs, may be confused
by the changing details in and position of
the brackets in which are shown a regiment's
sub-title – its colonelcy, role or number. How a
new title was constructed at a time
of change in role or amalgamation
was a matter of detailed discussion by senior
regimental officers balanced by the need for
standardisation set by the War Office, now the
Ministry of Defence; what the reader sees is
the outcome of often heated debate.

NOTE ON BRITISH ARMY REFORMS

Many of the regiments depicted in the book had been in existence for about two centuries by the time Seccombe was active as an artist, a few for less time but all had a proud and costly record of service to the Crown.

Shortcomings in the British Army, which became evident in the Crimean War, led to fundamental reforms being undertaken in the following thirty years. Besides other aspects of change the Reforms, led by two Secretaries of State for War, Edward Cardwell in the 1860s and Hugh Childers in the 1880s, resulted in the restructuring of the Army and its capacity to reinforce itself with reservists at times of crisis.

The reforms dispensed with the old system of identifying regiments by numbers and formally affiliated regiments with strong county ties to those counties. This latter aspect of policy led to those regiments with weak local ties being paired with unconnected or distant county regiments; an example of this is found with the 99th Duke of Edinburgh's (Lanarkshire) Regiment being paired with 62nd (Wiltshire) Regiment to become the Duke of Edinburgh's (Wiltshire Regiment) with a new depot in Devizes.

Further reforms introduced in 1906 by Richard Haldane, Secretary of State for War, were a result of lessons learned during the Boer Wars. The main elements of reform were to create an operational expeditionary force with headquarters, staff and supporting services and to restructure and strengthen the reserve forces to reinforce the expeditionary force at short notice. The rapid despatch of the British Expeditionary Force to France in 1914 stands witness to the success of these reforms.

Cavalry. By 1861 the difference in role and equipment between heavy and light cavalry had all but disappeared; regiments, armed with sword, carbine and pistol, operated in the same way; the only variation was that Lancer regiments kept their lances. There were twenty-eight cavalry regiments to which, in 1862, a further three were added from the European regiments which had been part of the Army of the Honourable East India Company. See Appendix 3 for the succession of regiments and their changing titles.

Infantry. In the 1860s, before the Cardwell Reforms, the infantry consisted of the three regiments of the Brigade of Guards (Grenadier, Coldstream, Scots Guards), 109 numbered infantry regiments of the line and The Rifle Brigade which had been taken out of the line in 1816. By the end of the Childers Reforms in the 1880s there remained the Brigade of Guards, The Rifle Brigade and sixty-seven regiments of the line with a county or local affiliation. Apart from the Brigade of Guards , the reforms broadly provided for each regiment to be established with two regular battalions, one for home and the other for overseas service, its own in-county or local training Depot and a third (reserve) Battalion, formed from a local militia or volunteer rifle regiment.

Continued

Development. The British Army has constantly changed to meet new threats and to adopt new technologies to take the fight to its enemies. We see this, amongst other examples, in the late 18th and early 19th centuries with the development of Light Cavalry, in the last four decades of the 19th century with the adoption of rifles, the Gatling and Maxim guns, the Royal Engineers' development of observation balloons, in 1912 with the inception of The Royal Flying Corps (RFC) and later in the First World War with the development of tanks. It should not be forgotten that, besides volunteers from other Corps, many officers and men from the Army's cavalry and infantry regiments transferred to the Tank Corps and to the RFC. The latter remained part of the Army until The Royal Air Force was established as a separate arm in April 1918.

Similarly, during and after the Second World War, the Special Air Service Regiment (1941), The Glider Pilot Regiment (1941-1957), The Parachute Regiment (1942), The Army Air Corps (1942/1957) were raised. In 2005, the Special Reconnaissance Regiment joined the order of battle.

Throughout the process of continuing change the British Army has steadfastly retained its regimental system which was refined in the second half of the 19th century. The importance of the regiment cannot be overstated and is best described by Sir Arthur Bryant (1899-1985). in his book 'Jackets of Green' (William Collins Sons & Co Ltd, 1972):—

"Pride of Regiment and love for the Regiment's history and tradition is the sacred Ark of the Covenant on which the British soldier depends in battle and on which Britain, through him, has again and again survived and won through to victory".

Sir Arthur Bryant CH CBE

Of the dates shown below against each Corps and Regiment, the first is the date from which its oldest antecedent regiment or component started continuous service to the Crown, the second or only date is either the date of its last amalgamation or formation.

THE LIFE GUARDS (1658/1922)
THE BLUES AND ROYALS (1661/1969)
THE HOUSEHOLD CAVALRY MOUNTED REGIMENT (1658/1992)
THE ROYAL HORSE ARTILLERY (1793)
including The King's Troop RHA (1946)*
1ST THE QUEEN'S DRAGOON GUARDS (1685/1959)
THE ROYAL SCOTS DRAGOON GUARDS (1661/1971)
THE ROYAL DRAGOON GUARDS (1685/1999)
THE QUEEN'S ROYAL HUSSARS (1685/1993)
THE ROYAL LANCERS (1689/2015)
THE KING'S ROYAL HUSSARS (1715/1992)
THE LIGHT DRAGOONS (1715/1992)
THE ROYAL TANK REGIMENT (1917/ 2014)
THE ROYAL YEOMANRY (1794/1967)
THE ROYAL WESSEX YEOMANRY (1794/1971)
THE QUEEN'S OWN YEOMANRY (1794/ 1971)
THE SCOTTISH AND NORTH IRISH YEOMANRY (1794/2014)
THE ROYAL REGIMENT OF ARTILLERY (1716/1924)
THE CORPS OF ROYAL ENGINEERS (1716, 1856)
THE CORPS OF ROYAL SIGNALS (1920)

GRENADIER GUARDS (1656/1665)
COLDSTREAM GUARDS (1661)
SCOTS GUARDS (1662)
IRISH GUARDS (1900)
WELSH GUARDS (1915)
LONDON REGIMENT (1908/1993)
(reserve battalion affiliated to the Foot Guards)
ROYAL REGIMENT OF SCOTLAND (1661/2006)
PRINCESS OF WALES'S ROYAL REGIMENT (1661/1992)
DUKE OF LANCASTER'S REGIMENT (1680/2006)
ROYAL REGIMENT OF FUSILIERS (1674/ 1968)
ROYAL ANGLIAN REGIMENT (1685/1968)
YORKSHIRE REGIMENT (1685/2006)
ROYAL WELSH (1689/ 2006)
MERCIAN REGIMENT (1689/2007)
ROYAL IRISH REGIMENT (1689/ 1992)
PARACHUTE REGIMENT (1942)
ROYAL GURKHA RIFLES (1858/1994)
RIFLES (1685/2007)
SPECIAL AIR SERVICE REGIMENT (1941)
ARMY AIR CORPS (1942/1957)

SPECIAL RECONNAISSANCE REGIMENT (2005)
ROYAL ARMY CHAPLAINS DEPARTMENT (1796)
ROYAL LOGISTICS CORPS (1794/ 1993)
ROYAL ARMY MEDICAL CORPS (1855)
ROYAL ELECTRICAL AND MECHANICAL ENGINEERS (1942)
ADJUTANT GENERAL'S CORPS (1846/1992)
ROYAL ARMY VETERINARY CORPS (1903)
SMALL ARMS SCHOOL CORPS (1854/1929)
ROYAL ARMY DENTAL CORPS (1921)
INTELLIGENCE CORPS (1940)
ROYAL ARMY PHYSICAL TRAINING CORPS (1860/1918)
GENERAL SERVICE CORPS (1914)
QUEEN ALEXANDRA'S ROYAL ARMY NURSING CORPS (1881/1949)
CORPS OF ARMY MUSIC (1857/2006)
ROYAL MONMOUTHSHIRE ROYAL ENGINEERS (1539/1661/1967)**
HONOURABLE ARTILLERY COMPANY (1537/1661)**
ROYAL GIBRALTAR REGIMENT (1958/1991)
ROYAL BERMUDA REGIMENT (1894/1965)

*The Household Cavalry takes precedence and parades on the right of the line; an exception to this is made when the Royal Horse Artillery is on parade with its guns in which case it takes precedence.

** These regiments' date of origin is so ancient as to be included although their continuous service to the Crown must necessarily date from the establishment of the England's Standing Army in 1661.

APPENDIX 3

SUCCESSION OF CAVALRY & ARMOURED REGIMENTS

DATE OF ESTABLISHMENT IN ROYAL SERVICE	AMALGAMATIONS BY 1970	21ST CENTURY SUCCESSOR REGIMENT
1ST LIFE GUARDS (1658)	THE LIFE GUARDS	THE LIFE GUARDS
2ND LIFE GUARDS (1659)		
ROYAL HORSE GUARDS (THE BLUES) (1661)	THE BLUES AND ROYALS (ROYAL HORSE GUARDS AND 1ST DRAGOONS)	THE BLUES AND ROYALS (ROYAL HORSE GUARDS AND 1ST DRAGOONS)
1ST ROYAL DRAGOONS (THE ROYALS) (1661)		
1ST KING'S DRAGOON GUARDS (1685)	1ST QUEEN'S DRAGOON GUARDS	1ST THE QUEEN'S DRAGOON GUARDS
2ND DRAGOON GUARDS (QUEEN'S BAYS) (1685)		
3RD (PRINCE OF WALES) DRAGOON GUARDS (1685)	ROYAL SCOTS DRAGOON GUARDS (CARABINIERS AND GREYS)	THE ROYAL SCOTS DRAGOON GUARDS (CARABINIERS AND GREYS)
6TH DRAGOON GUARDS (CARABINIERS) (1685)		
2ND DRAGOONS (ROYAL SCOTS GREYS) (1681)		
4TH (ROYAL IRISH) DRAGOON GUARDS (1685)	4TH/7TH DRAGOON GUARDS	THE ROYAL DRAGOON GUARDS
7TH (PRINCESS ROYAL'S) DRAGOON GUARDS (1688)		
5TH (PRINCESS CHARLOTTE OF WALES'S) DRAGOON GUARDS (1685)	5TH ROYAL INNISKILLING DRAGOONS	
6TH (INNISKILLING) DRAGOONS (1689)		
3RD (THE KING'S OWN) HUSSARS (1685)	QUEEN'S OWN HUSSARS	THE QUEEN'S ROYAL HUSSARS (QUEEN'S OWN AND ROYAL IRISH)
7TH (QUEEN'S OWN) HUSSARS (1689)		
4TH (QUEEN'S OWN) HUSSARS (1685)	QUEEN'S ROYAL IRISH HUSSARS	
8TH (KING'S ROYAL IRISH) HUSSARS (1693)		

DATE OF ESTABLISHMENT IN ROYAL SERVICE	AMALGAMATIONS BY 1970	21ST CENTURY SUCCESSOR REGIMENT
9TH (QUEEN'S ROYAL) LANCERS (1715)	9TH/12 ROYAL LANCERS (PRINCE OF WALES'S)	THE ROYAL LANCERS (QUEEN ELZABETH'S OWN)
12TH (PRINCE OF WALES'S ROYAL) LANCERS (1715)		
5TH (ROYAL IRISH) LANCERS (1858)	16TH/5TH QUEEN'S ROYAL LANCERS	
16TH (QUEEN'S) LANCERS (1759)		
17TH (DUKE OF CAMBRIDGE'S OWN) LANCERS (1759)	17TH/21ST LANCERS	
21ST (EMPRESS OF INDIA'S) LANCERS (1858)		
10TH (PRINCE OF WALES'S OWN ROYAL) HUSSARS (1715)	ROYAL HUSSARS (PRINCE OF WALES'S OWN)	THE KING'S ROYAL HUSSARS
11TH (PRINCE ALBERT'S OWN) HUSSARS (1715)		
14TH (KINGS) HUSSARS (1715)	14TH/20TH KING'S HUSSARS	
20TH HUSSARS (1858)		
13TH HUSSARS (1715)	13/18TH ROYAL HUSSARS (QUEEN MARY'S OWN)	THE LIGHT DRAGOONS
18TH (QUEEN MARY'S OWN) HUSSARS (1759)		
15TH (THE KING'S) HUSSARS (1759)	15TH/19TH KING'S ROYAL HUSSARS	
19TH (QUEEN ALEXANDRA'S OWN ROYAL) HUSSARS (1858)		
THE TANK CORPS (1917)	ROYAL TANK REGIMENT	THE ROYAL TANK REGIMENT

THE TEAM

Paul Cordle, who lives in Wiltshire, served in the Grenadier Guards during the 1960s and 1970s; since acquiring an 1880 edition of Seccombe's book over forty years ago he has been keen to make it available to a wider audience. The project to achieve this has been carried out in collaboration with Jan Kalinowski who also lives in Wiltshire and served in the Territorial Army with the Royal Artillery and with Anthony Weldon who lives in London and served in the Irish Guards in the 1960s.

MESS ART

'Mess Art' is able to provide mounted giclée prints and various household items using Seccombe's illustrations. For details please visit

www.mess-art.co.uk

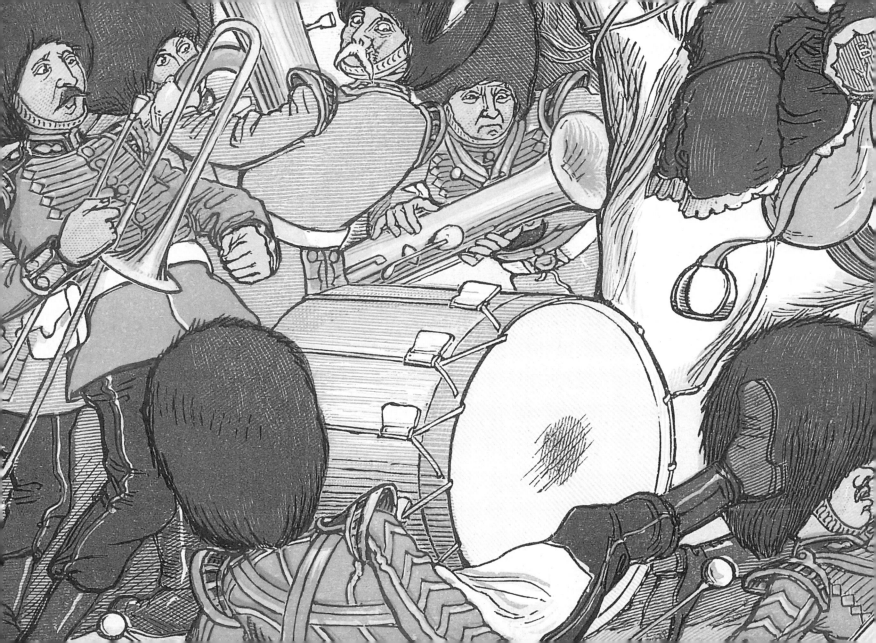

Peter Gregory March 1st - 1986

C000184242

*High
on
Hope*

GWYN THOMAS

High on Hope

Extracts from the *Western Mail* Articles
edited by
Jeffrey Robinson and Brian McCann

D. BROWN AND SONS
COWBRIDGE
1985

© 1985 Jeffrey Robinson and Brian McCann

ISBN 0 905928 40 7

DESIGNED AND PRINTED IN WALES BY
D. Brown & Sons Ltd., Bridgend, Mid Glamorgan

Contents

Dedication

To Lyn, without whose efforts
much of her husband's published work
would not have appeared.

With affectionate good wishes.

Foreword

Gwyn Thomas, who died in 1981, was born on 6th July 1913 in Cymmer near Porth in the Rhondda Valley, the son of a miner—'an underground ostler with no love of coal and no luck with horses'. He was the youngest of twelve children. His mother died when he was six and he was brought up by his older sister, Nana. In 1930 a State Scholarship took him from Porth Grammar School to St. Edmund Hall, Oxford to study modern languages and a Miners' Scholarship later enabled him to study for six months in Madrid before graduating in 1934.

His first job was as a lecturer for the Workers Educational Association in South Wales. Then after his marriage to Lyn Thomas in 1938 he worked as a social service officer in Lancashire and Cheshire before going to Cardigan Grammar School as French master in 1940. In 1942 he moved to Barry Grammar School where he taught Spanish for the next twenty years before devoting himself entirely to writing and broadcasting.

Although Gwyn Thomas began writing soon after coming down from Oxford, it was not until after the war that his wife sent three of his manuscripts to publishers. These met with instant success when in 1946 he had published 'Where Did I Put my Pity?' and 'The Dark Philosophers' and in the following year 'The Alone to the Alone'.

He was a prolific writer. Everything was written in long hand in excercise books and then typed by his wife. Eventually he filled about five-hundred of these books, with fourteen novels and collections of short stories, numerous radio and television plays, stage plays and essays for a variety of national and international magazines.

For several years Gwyn contributed a regular Saturday column in the *Western Mail*, together with occasional feature articles. The items in this book are taken entirely from that source and we are most grateful to the *Western Mail* for giving us permission to reproduce these edited extracts.

The Saturday column, ostensibly a criticism of the week's television served mainly as a launching pad from which Gwyn was able to take off on many and varied tangents. This volume is intended as one for the reader to dip into to rediscover his unique style. Those of us who enjoyed his company and who knew the private man as well as the public performer, recall with undiminished pleasure his sparkling conversation, with his ability to change the tone in a word from one of fearsome indignation to exploding hilarity, making full use of his vast vocabulary to create word pictures in a dazzlingly inventive and original manner. Happily many of his utterances have been preserved as a result of his numerous television and radio broadcasts, but at the time of writing we find it incredible that most of his work is out of print.

On a purely personal level we recall his surprising shyness, his kindness, his compassion but above all that sharp and imaginative perception of humour, which continued to shine with unfailing enthusiasm long after his health began giving cause for concern. He once wrote 'In the darkest night of the spirit, laughter is the signal that we are fully and unconquerably still there. And when a fine laughter maker falls still, the night itself for a while, will be inconsolable'. Only now do we fully appreciate what he meant.

Jeffrey Robinson
March, 1985   Brian McCann

Ritual Ululations

A strict Sunday School upbringing curbed my interest in harems. The region was wrong for such antics. The ethos was too libertarian and the houses generally too small. Any man trying to keep a clutch of subservient women in the parlour, summoned by hooter and organised in shifts on the lines of pit-labour, would have had a hard time of it. Any attempt to impose an Islamic pattern on marriage would have had the aspiring Welsh sheikh dangling dead from the hump of his tallest camel well before dawn.

So it was with special attention that I watched the documentary 'Behind the Veil'. This showed us a harem in the Sheikhdom of Dubai. The Crown Prince was being married. The gift from his father was a million dollars, which gives marriage a whole new point. The father's income is five hundred million dollars a year. Mohammed, instead of sending his armies of conquering zealots into Europe and Asia, should have waited for oil and travelled in style.

We heard the wedding songs. Musically, the ritual ululations of Islam must have set a record for maddening monotony before the coming of pop music. We heard snatches of Arab poetry. The moon is paradise. The moon is an oasis of honeyed fountains, inviolable calm. Maidens eternally young and bridegrooms tirelessly aroused. We know better now, but it was a nice thought while it lasted. The veils get smaller as men's conceit gets less preposterous, and oil-sponsored activities provide them with alternative hobbies to bossing one harem.

We saw the wedding feast: raisins from Damascus, tin from Tyre, nectar from Nineveh, biscuits from London and cockles, no doubt from Penclawdd. One had the suggestion of an appalling stew of jealously, boredom and waste. I was reminded of a cartoon showing a bored and exhausted sheikh surrounded by a cluster of eager and lovely wives. To the one nearest him he says, 'I love you. Pass it round.'

I would say that on balance the Sunday School was more bracing. A repeated chorus of 'Calon Lân' probably set more intense vibrations going than anything that happened in the shadow of the mosque or the voluptuous rhythms of the Seraglio. At least, to say so shows a healthy attitude.

Here is an odd fact. Wales, for a century past, has had for a large part of its popular culture a thunderous spate of pulpit rhetoric against drink and sex. Yet the two Welsh artists who have carried the name of Wales most resonantly around the world, Augustus John and Dylan Thomas, marched impenitently through life under the banner of unrestricted alcohol and a free wheeling libido. A considerable part of the Welsh community would still prissily dismiss them as arrogant lepers, which shows how little we know about leprosy.

It's a Knock-Out

Europe, in its long and reeling past, has seen some rum kinds of human conduct. The glare and crackle of madness have never been far away from its eyes and tongue. But poverty, pollution, weariness, television and crumbling frontiers will bring a kind of wisdom. Repeated enough, even persecution and murder, those two most cherished hobbies of man, begin to lose their savour.

We are not likely to see again the peaks of criminal folly that make European history so hard a slog. We've priced ourselves out of the more spectacular idiocies of yesteryear. We would have to save for a hundred years to afford another respectable war. Lovers of trench warfare and blitzkrieg will have to rely for their future kicks on some suave bits of chiselling in the roulette rooms of the common market.

So we look around for quieter and cheaper aberrations. One such has been found in a television programme called 'Jeux sans Frontières'. This is an extension into Europe of a British game called 'It's a Knock-Out'. It is not as dire as the dispatch into Europe of our expeditionary forces in '14 and '39, but it tries hard to get into that league.

The programme consists of setting contestants crass tasks that will make them look as foolish as possible and one is left at the end with the conviction that man's capacity for embarrassment and martyrdom is one of his lasting glories. Evolutionary time wastes two million years in converting Monkeys into Men and a revel of this competitive sort can reverse the process in half an hour. The programme never closes without my having a mental glimpse of Lamarck, Darwin and Thomas Huxley shaking hands gravely with Eddie Waring and saying they might have been wrong after all.

Prodigious ingenuity must go into the devising of the imbecilic challenges which confront the teams that come from every corner of Europe to take part in this macabre joust. Since the First Crusade, the Relief of Mafeking and the Nuremberg Rallies there has been no such climax of ecstasy and dementia. What the baroque stands for in architecture, these romps achieve in television.

It is difficult to pick out and recall firm details from the cataract of absurdities. I think I remember teams of cyclists trying to pedal through a lagoon of glue, a lighted wick projecting from each ear, holding a loaded pint glass in one hand and playing 'Now Let A Smile Be Your Umbrella' as a flute solo with the other. Recently one of the tests was to put on four overcoats and a very tall hat and walk under a low bar along an upended plank. After that no one should find the Balance of Payments a problem.

As I stare at these marvels I am reminded of school sports and a boy called Spurgeon. He was a timid boy and a shivering claustrophobic. Relays of boys had to be sent to fetch him from the toilet that had a stiff catch. The gross arrogance and exhibitionism of sports day had him making tentative leaps under the nearest bus.

But persuasion by the headmaster and some brutal coercion from the Physical Education man recruited Spurgeon into the obstacle race. The first obstacle was a vast tarpaulin tightly nailed to the ground under which the contestants had to crawl. I saw Spurgeon's face, blue with shocked bewilderment, come pelting out of that pall a dozen times, wondering if he had changed planets as a new after-lunch novelty meant to ginger up the school meals service.

The P.E. man gave Spurgeon a fix on direction by putting his boot on his canopied rump. Then there was a bottle of pop to be swigged while walking in a sack, then a half pint of milk to be drunk while hanging upside down, then a cream bun to be eaten while climbing through a suspended tyre. It was from the inside of the tyre, taking frenetic nibbles at the bun, that we fetched Spurgeon back to the land of his normal fears.

If the Vale of Glamorgan entered for the next 'Jeux Sans

Frontières', my scouts will sweep Britain in search of Spurgeon. After bracing him with a pint of half-and-half, dark ale and adrenalin mixed, I would keep him in reserve for the climactic event, eating a whole Caerphilly cheese and humming the Hallellujah Chorus inside a barrel at the further end of the deepest of Ystradfellte's caves.

The thought that must haunt the mind of a stand-up comedian is that he would have done better to remain seated.

*

They even have correspondence courses in the technique of stand-up comedy. Judging by some of the comedy turns one sees, some of the aspirants drop the correspondence course in the early stages and take their jokes direct from the postman.

*

To this day a tremulous anxiety has been a strong ingredient among men who deliberately embark on the satanic craft of making other people laugh.

The Sovereign Opiate

Total clarity is one thing humanity has never been able to afford. Every age, every society finds ways of averting its eyes from its essential realities, on the few chilly occasions when they are glimpsed. Mass religious observance, the lyrical self-absorption of prayer, the patient awaiting of seasonal holocausts, the terror-taboos of witch-medicine, the cretinous clarion-blasts of the tribe militant, all have done their bit in slicing bright-eyed awareness down to the minimum necessary to get us in and out of the house and keep the mortgage cool.

Now they all step back to acknowledge the king of them all, the sovereign opiate and ether drip of twentieth century man. Television sport. Every Saturday the Jivaro Indians of both channels shrink the national head by a clear inch.

Even sex and greed, greatly ingenious as they have been in the promotion of bliss, have been heard to concede total victory to horses and athletes. I would say that show-jumping alone has introduced a feudal simplicity into our collective thinking that has set political speculation back a hundred years. I once prophesied that John Wayne's horse would one day be the next Vice-President of the United States, and I see no reason to withdraw the forecast.

I am not complaining. I once knew an aged lady. She was imperious and crotchetty. She could never catch a glimpse of joy without wishing to confound it and rattle it out of court. Then in the last year of her life she came to know cricket on the box. She had never seen the game before. She fell totally under its spell. She watched every second of the long transmissions. The tranquil enchantment in white and green, the ordered sociable ballet of the players' moves, the priestly assurance of the umpires' coats, took her mind off the pain that was edging her remorsely away from life. She had found the antidote to the poison of selfish fuss that had made a grey waste of her days. And her existence, when it and the cricket season ended, did so in the most marvellous and unlikely radiance of a spirit ecstatically at peace.

Snooker is a game played on a table with balls and long sticks. It put me in mind of that lady. I understood little of the game's rules and intentions. I was only once at a snooker table for a few seconds in the Upper Rhondda. The table's cloth was one of the most ancient bits of fabric even in that time and place of scarcity. Only the oldest and most loyal members of the Welfare Hall claimed that it had once been recognisably green. Legend was that it had been bought second-hand from the first Rothschild, and transported secretly from the Champs Elysées to the Rhondda Fach.

I played only one stroke on that table. It was a swooping, decisive move that should, with a better alphabet of luck, have spelled mastery. The end of the shot found the ball untouched and a piece of cloth the size of a door waving in the air like a bullfighter's cloak. I reached the safety of a passing tram with a posse of baying committee men and snooker-addicts at my heels. Now, calm and in no mood any further to misplace cue-balls and misuse cues, I salute the incredible if narrow artistry of the men who practise their form of yoga around the baize.

A passionate sporting enthusiasm though can be an unsettling thing. I know people who have gone through life in the most remiss manner, their minds given up to endless summer-tinted memories of all the summer games they played in youth. An addiction to rugby football can be every bit as paralysing, for the addict as well as for the people on whom he loads the details of his phobia. But not everyone will respond with the same sentimental eagerness to these sagas of physical hardness, linament, dressing-rooms jokes and epic beer-swilling as the man who, in these terms, is constructing a loving memorial to his own lost youth and failing prowess.

Boxers, as long as they are not boxing, interest me. I

believe, as did Dr. Summerskill, that the impulse to clip other people under the jaw is regressive and deplorable. The normal encounters of life rattle and curdle the human brain well enough without help from fisticuffs. In a world that has so many dedicated athletes who afflict the muscles of the envious and the conscience of the idle with an equal ache, I warm to any athlete who is utterly inept.

I once watched a fight between Alberto Lovell and Joe Bugner. Alberto hugged his opponent like a clumsy seducer, and the affair moved to its finish in a sort of broken waltz tempo. I thank Alberto. He was an inspiration to the ailing and the aged. His way of falling to the ground without help from his adversary was a lesson in the art of simplifying violence.

But the sight of constant vitality has always made me uneasily cautious. In such concentrations as the Olympics, it gave me an urge to crouch for a week or two in the nearest crypt.

After watching a ration of diving, rowing and hockey I moved without complaint to a circus programme from Blackpool, where abnormal physical movement was at least directed to frank and sensible commercial ends. I saw a lady in mid-air balancing a sword on a dagger. That could be a good hint, for there are not all that many things to do in mid-air.

There was a platoon of the brightest looking dogs, The Perky Pekes, I have ever seen. With a little more height, less tongue and tidier habits, they could run a borough. And there were the clowns who were, as always, next to cows, the saddest creatures under the sun.

Later, still hooked on the high-level Olympic convulsions, I watched swimming until I felt threatened and put on my life-belt to slip out for a glass. I distrust all sports like swimming at which young people can do supernormally well.

During the opening parade I was struck by the country which had just two athletes. Slow, grave men they were, wearing thickly striped pantaloons and looking as if they had done their first practice sprints getting away from a chain gang. After all that swimming my mind will take a month to get dry. In moments of gloom I feel I could swap the whole legion of human swimmers, divers and jumpers for one good dolphin.

I must say that my interest in athletics has been sharpened by all the talk of drugs that can alter the physical scope of athletes. I cannot now watch an eight stone girl athlete without a whimsical conviction that she is, without chemical prompting, a fourteen stone bearded male fitter, shaven and shrunk for just that day.

When the soporific miracle of Wimbledon hits the nation I light out for the hills or take out my diving suit for another whack at finding the drowned city of Kenfig. I am sorry about this. I wish I could enter this vast enchantment and ease the carping watchfulness of my nerves.

There is no doubt that those great audiences at Wimbledon, sitting motionless except for that hypnotised wagging of the head, are on to a good thing. They are beyond earthly cares. When those tremendous slices of tennis are on the air, Britons are subjugated in a way not known since the Romans went. These intense crouching heroes who stare at each other over the nets, are a new kind of world-hero, supplanting utterly and more or less benignly, the warriors and bandits who inspired the affection and terror of yesterday.

If Butch Cassidy and the Sundance Kid had lived just a bit later they would almost certainly have made it to the Centre Court for a bigger clean-up than they ever made in their traffic with banks, shooting no more sheriffs, just bruising the odd, impercipient umpire.

I am sure that during certain phases of this plop-plop saga, most of the intrigues and delusions that motivate politics and business go into the fridge for later use, and even the normal ecstasies of physical love are told to wait until the current game is settled.

It makes me regret even more bitterly that on one strange, sunstruck day of my adolescence I got all the summer sports confused into an inscrutable mess. During my short encounter with cricket we had a player who could make the ball come in sharply off the rock-face. He concussed me twice. At the school sports I flattened so many hurdles they abolished the event and switched me to the marathon where I was reported lost for a week.

So when I got my sunstroke and took up a little rudimentary tennis, I found myself skying the ball over Dowlais and leaping over the net when there was no conceivable reason for doing so. And when I became an apprentice member of the bowls team I developed an over-arm way of delivering the wood that caused the groundsman to warn me that if I did not stop doing serious damage to the green, he would do even more serious damage to me. I swallowed the jack and left.

The Olympics are a plot to keep our energy from slipping below taxable levels.

*

I confess myself allergic to table-tennis. Once, long ago, as the result of a faulty telephone connection, I found myself holding the amateur wardenship of a boys' club and ping-pong had been recommended as part of the ritual initiation into manhood. We also had a chess course in the club. Either the boys had not been given the rules of this game or they used lapsing into coma as a fixed tactic. I was worn out by the double strain of sedating demonic ping-pong players and applying the mirror test to the motionless lips of chess players marooned in some fathomless meditation.

*

The colour of the snooker table fascinates me. Having an allergy to lawn mowers, I find a deep calm in the sight of anything green that doesn't grow.

*

There's something in our weather that is hostile to treats, feasts and outings. After a childhood largely spent in strapping on life-belts made of the more buoyant sheet-music in drenched eisteddfod marquees, I am gloomy about the sky when jollity is on the agenda.

Let it be Utter

The moon, for a time was on everybody's screen and most people's minds. I'm afraid I lag behind the vibrant ecstasy that came pouring out of the Apollo studios. I tend to be a Little Earther. Patrick Moore's eyebrows do not hold me in thrall nor do I believe, as some do, that the heavenly bodies move in rhythm with their brilliant twitching.

As I looked at that landscape of desolation on which the astronauts landed, I fell victim to a gloomy theory. That dusty wilderness is just a front, a deception. There may not be people on the moon, in sight, because they are all inside, out of the weather and dispensing with air. During these moon landings they all stay quiet as mice, waiting for the human nuisance to abate. As soon as they hear the retro-rockets blasting the interlopers back to their own uneasy clinker, they amble out, make a reckoning of the rocks that have been stolen, then return to their warrens lamenting the folly of a species that insists, as we do, on living on the rough, vulnerable crust of its star. One of these nights a full moon will show a new inscription. 'You Have Deserts Of Your Own. Stay There. Signed: The Lunar Preservation Society and Home Guard.'

I heard of a man on the Saturday night of the first moonwalk. He came home brimful of ale and more than usually dense. His wife had gone to bed, worn out by astronomy. He switched on the set. Through the alcoholic fog he watched the astronauts lurching and levitating in their improbable suits. The next morning he told his wife, 'These old films on the box get worse and worse. Last night was "Abbott and Costello Under Water". I'd seen it before. Terrible.' I liked that. If we are to have confusion, let it be utter.

As a precocious boy in a community where plentiful disease gave the only hint of family planning, I proceeded almost without pause from comics to the works of that sourest of economists, Malthus. He was convinced that humanity was eating itself out of house and home. Whenever he saw a woman showing the slightest sign of fertility, he would go off his food for days on end to redress the balance.

*

Amateur opera generates more happiness than amateur drama because it mobilises more people and is more liable to the heightened comradeship of shared disaster.

Scenery tends to fall, costumes, inaccurately ordered, split down the back or fall off in the middle of a ringing note, inadequate voices are severely taxed: but always, in retrospect, a cordial and lovable escapade.

*

It is sad that so much South Welsh talent should have had to grow from such a pungent compost of early mutilations.

*

Once in Caerphilly an American drew my attention to a monstrous bulge in one of the walls. I put it down to a regional tendency to hernia. The visitor, not knowing of the Welsh taste for inaccuracy, made a solemn note of it.

Confusion as a Culture in Itself

I've always been interested in the way pleasure has been distributed, the incidence of bliss. Some people go through life without seeming to have one single good draught of it. Others appear to bathe in it from birth to death, shattering their friends with claps of laughter, tapping freshets of glee from every situation that comes along.

As a dowser of felicity I have not done too well. In a place as earnestly unsure of itself as Wales, seekers after a perennial gusto and loose-fitting rapture stand to get their shins rapped hard. Outcrops of anxiety from the past keep the present in a twitch and send us lurching out of plumb.

I have tried at odd times to find a seat on this or that wing of traditional Welsh enthusiasm and got consistently shaken off.

In my boyhood, religious revivalism on the classic scale was, like almost everything else in our society at the time, running out of breath. When one of the last of the great evangelical mystagogues was working his spell in our town, I became one of his principal solo singers and banner bearers.

With my alto rendering of 'Have Courage My Boy To Say No' I maddened drunkards and adulterers with shame for their lapses, and brought the devout pouring through the chapel gates. The evangelist promised me a rich reward not in heaven but here, in spending money.

In the very middle of his mission he up and went off to California to marry a well-heeled widow of Welsh extraction. That experience combined with a deteriorating diet threw me into the arms of the sceptics.

Once or twice I have sidled up to rugby football. There is no doubt that in consideration of Welsh culture one has to conclude that this game, with its instant melodrama and its magnets of remembrance, has drained off much of the ardour that might have gone into a more sedulous cultivation of the arts.

The only rugby with which I was personally associated was of a boring brutality that produced nothing but two first-aid brigades, which won medals and cups and the Crossed Splints award with oakleaves.

I was never a player but mastered a booklet on how to be a rugby referee. I officiated at one match. My nerves were bad and my whistle seemed to possess a loud and wilful life of its own. The players became convinced that I was blowing them to order for being underclothed. In the second half they buried their differences and chased me down the hillside to a suitable lynching area.

One of the curious strains in the cultural dilemma of the Welsh is summed up in the melancholy face of a woman I once knew. Her grandfather had been a leading thinker and organiser of the Syndicalist movement for trade-union control of industry which dominated Welsh radicalism in the years that led up to the First World War.

She saved up enough money to provide a memorial plaque to him and a library of political works for a local Labour Club.

She entrusted the money to her son, a man numb to any intellectual excitement that by-passed the *Football Echo*. He blew the money on a trip to New Zealand and Fiji to see a Lions tour that featured a preponderance of Welsh players. His mother ordered a mourning garland and a slow rendering of 'The Red Flag' laced with bits of 'Llef'.

I think the Welsh would have benefited from a spell of totally mindless hedonism. A man in my town was a strong enemy of Welshness. He believed that our minds had become waterlogged by the tears of a too sentimental piety and blown shapeless by too windy a political rhetoric.

He had some spare cash and dreamed of becoming a Tory demagogue after the style of Joseph Chamberlain. He wanted to take the town's mind off the fears raised by the slump that started in Wall Street, America, and ran in a straight line to Dinas, Rhondda Fawr.

He decided to start a soccer team. 'Rugby players tend to talk Welsh,' he said. 'I don't want them. That oval ball is the symbol of deviousness. A round, candid ball and no pawing of bodies, that's the honest English way.'

The soccer did not flourish. The pitch was riven by subsidence and the dirt surface collapsed beneath the striker's feet when he was poised to score his only goal of the season.

The man's dreams switched to a greyhound track. Gambling fever and the excited yelps of panting hounds and the sheen of bookies' bowlers would have our branch of the Celtic family leaping clear of our chronic posture of debate and defiance.

I attended the opening night. I badly needed distraction. My mind was under fire from a variety of artillery parks. My friends at the Workmen's Hall were Stalinists to a man, even urging people filing into the convenience on the square to respect the Popular Front.

Against them was ranged my father. As a youth he had been strongly touched by the 'Cymru Fydd', Home Rule movement of Tom Ellis and Lloyd George. Now, in his rather withered twilight, after a middle period of tepid devotion to the gracious graduation of Ramsay Macdonald, the old dreams of Welsh resurgence were beginning to gild his life again.

He approached me one day looking very thoughtful. He touched his rather full moustache which he had grown as a tribute to Ramsay Macdonald. He said: 'I didn't grow this in servile imitation of that courtly flatterer who leads the Labour Party. This moustache is the very twin and image of the moustache worn by the heroic Celtic Chieftain Caractacus which I saw in a book called 'Torch Bearers of Welsh History' in the Institute.

'I hope it gives me the same sad, pensive air it gave Caractacus. Be inspired by it. And about that argument we had last night. Forget about that Stalin and those onion

- 24 -

domes of the Kremlin. Put your money on Llewellyn Bren who played hell with the Normans in the Caerphilly area and was executed by them in Cardiff on the very spot where James Howells' store stands now. That's where I'll do all my shopping from now on if I'll ever manage to get the trainfare to Cardiff again. Howells . . . In memory of Llewellyn Bren. That Stalin is a bit of a Norman, if you ask me.'

So on that first night at the dogs I was in a mood to break free from racial nostalgia and scientific positivism. The pro-Saxon promoter of the stadium took me to one side. 'Bet a bundle on the big, black dog in the sixth race. His name is Cromwell, after Oliver the Roundhead, who trounced the Welsh at St. Fagans.'

I put sixpence, my fag money for the rest of the week, on Cromwell. He would not have taken longer getting out of the trap if he had been easing himself out of a top security gaol. When he finally did so, he relieved himself against the railings with a disdain that took in men and running dogs.

I told my father. He was pleased. 'Quite right,' he said. 'Stop waiting for the Red Dawn to come rattling down on the tram from Cwm Maerdy. The dawn, when it comes, will be green. Its bringer will be Llewellyn Bren. This time he will avoid St. Mary Street where he fell foul of fate and fed the blood lust of the conqueror. He will recharge the lacerated old Welsh veins of Glamorgan. He might even give you a sense of true identity, you poor lost Anglicised loon.

The Welsh Resurgence is in full flood and I've missed the joy-ride again. I see people around me touched by the ecstasy of new beginnings. I stand on the side-lines, baffled.

I hear of areas in North Wales being made safe for pure Welshness, of traditional Welsh culture slipped like fluoride into social intercourse to prevent English caries.

I am told of sub-postmasters harassed and their stamps

degummed because they do not speak Welsh. And I, a product of the colossal fusion of landless peasants from West Wales and South-West England, can only marvel.

What has astonished me most about the attempted reconquest of Glamorgan and Gwent has been the barbarous division of our children on language grounds. Parents have told me with a most sinister glint of pride in their eyes, that their children are taxied and bussed five or ten miles to privileged special academies where they will not be contaminated by the children of their rough English speaking neighbours.

This is the worst wound you can inflict on a community. Welsh patriots have often boasted that with landed gentry so thin on the Jacobinical Welsh ground, we would never commit the sin of snobbish separatism implicit in the English Public School system. Yet a growing and muttering multitude see in the Welsh Schools simulations of Eton and Harrow. A Welsh Lord Rosebery, totally insulated from the Anglophone proles, is being concocted at this moment along the banks of the Taff. God help us.

The valleys of South-East Wales had, by the beginning of World War Two, gone over totally to the English-speaking world. The attempt to degrade and replace English in the schools of those areas will do nothing but mischief in minds already plagued by every neurosis that comes with insecurity. Bilingualism, pushed to the ultimate, will complete the work of spoliation and ruin begun by the coal-owners, and the collapse into dereliction of their weird kingdom.

The passionate social and academic drives of the valleys in their prime will be lost in places slumped between the stools of two imperfectly mastered tongues. The society that produced a small army of Aneurin Bevans will be lucky to come up with one darts champion and a few penillion* groups of second rank.

---

*   Traditional Welsh singing of verse in counterpoint to a well known melody.

Compassion is Catching On

From the first moment of self-recognition, humanity has been looking for some recipe for comradely benevolence. They probably thought they were on to a winner when they stumbled on alcoholic drink. Then the hardest-working researcher developed delirium tremens and they came to the conclusion that if it could not be achieved through the spirit alone the euphoria game was not worth the candle.

The next sensible view of a species gifted with the infliction and receipt of suffering has always been active concern for people in unbearable distress. Quite overtly during this century the distress has tended to outrun and outwit the concern. But compassion, after a rough first million years, has caught on and is never again likely to go under.

Even on the lowest level of pragmatism more and more people are coming to realise that being nice, tolerant and kindly, passes the time on more agreeably than being a ruffianly curmudgeon who goes down a new road only in the hope of finding someone groaning by the wayside on whom he can practise his skilled indifference.

A village in South East England was celebrating a Royal occasion. A bonfire had been built on the village green to take any little republican nip out of the July air. Tables loaded with dainties awaited the junior patriots. Tea-urns bubbled in a state of Canaveral readiness.

The only person absent from the loyal throng was a frail widow in her nineties. She stayed secluded in her thatched cottage alongside the village green. The bonfire was lit and was blazing beautifully. Then a hostile elf, sour against tribal joy and commemorative jellies, took a hand. The wind changed. Sparks floated on to the thatch of the widow's cottage. Prompt action rescued the old lady but the dwelling was ruined in an hour.

The revels were called off. The first rage became a

passion to heal the event. Relatives gave the widow shelter. The villagers laboured throughout the summer to rebuild the cottage. Three months after the disaster the Jubilee feast was held, and the widow was installed in her new home. 'We'd not been so happy since the end of the War.'

By an act of collective enthusiasm something pleasant was made to rise from the pile of ashes thematic in human affairs. Tiny acts of sympathetic response are the coral which will make the final reef of protection around our threatened kind.

The creative mind is a flower in search of its natural air of unconditional freedom. It can perish at any moment from the crude blades and stifling hoods of bigoted authority. Anything that divides men stupefies mankind.

*

Literature is basically the great freemasonry of loneliness. Writers wait for you. When a book is written the writer calls out in an empty street. For many years to come odd people come and answer the call. This silent intercourse is incomparably the most precious element in human existence.

Jesus of Nazareth

The television sky was bright with visual beauty and dark with moral concern for the showing of 'Jesus of Nazareth.' It left the eye and the mind exhausted with admiration and pity.

The director of 'Jesus', Franco Zeffirelli, has been famous in the theatre for contriving sets and scenes as densely rich in texture and colour as any of the great Renaissance paintings. He used this gift to brilliant ends in depicting the final episodes of the Gospel story. The scene of the Sanhedrin, the highest judicial court of the Jews, gave us one of the most fascinating and disquieting groups ever caught by television cameras.

Here were men speared on a barbarous crisis of fear and doubt. Their citadel had been shaken by a merciless wind. Holding power at the nod of an army of occupation, they had listened to the most blistering assault ever levelled against an established authority. No custodian of the public welfare enjoys being told that he is a tomb, all calm and dignity outside, all death and mouldering irrelevance within.

All the eyes in that crowded chamber, and they were some of the most expressive eyes in the theatrical world, fused into a perfect cloudscape of bewilderment, sorrow, malice and impatience, the main ingredients in the dish of any human situation but raised here to a level of almost intolerable tension. Even the beards became part of a supernormal and oppressive upholstery.

After the stifling immersion in the vile games men play to keep their illusions and privileges watertight for a few days more, the scenes of the betrayal, trial and death had a stunning desolation. The encounter between Christ and Pontius Pilate was magnificent. No greater tragedy can befall two human beings than to be mutually and eternally incomprehensible. They stood within moral and intellectual systems more distant from each other than any two planets. Jesus came to tell men that they could be saved and they were not saved.

Pilate came to tell men that they could be taxed and they were taxed. For Jesus humanity was a dream about to be realised. For Pilate, dusty, crotchetty, shuffling the blue chips of his inevitable promotion, humanity was a failure on its way to becoming a bore. The flowering heart of an empire will lead one to cynicism. The empire's scruffy edges can lead one only to despair.

I would express my final appreciation of the film in these terms. Let television now give us, keeping as near the grain of hard, non-denominational reality as possible, an assessment of the forces that fused Jesus, John the Baptist and Judas Iscariot into one single astounding historical act.

Mike Yarwood must be responsible for half the unemployment among actors.

*

Nurse Cavell said of patriotism what Mae West said of the average man: it is not enough.

*

A.S. Neill explaining his distrust of formal religion said: 'If I had been born in Baghdad I would have been a Muslim and forbidden whisky. Being able to have three wives instead I would have regarded as deplorably inadequate compensation'. Homo in one of his rare phases of sapience.

*

Television is, among other things, a sieve in which the significant faces and voices of our time are endlessly shaken. Some will find their appointed hole of doom and slip promptly through. Most of the others, as memories blur and critical standards tighten, will follow them to oblivion. A few will defy the sieve's mesh and hang around for what will seem an eternity.

On People . . .

Aneurin Bevan

The stammer was an enormously important element in the making of Bevan. The fault so tormented him that in his very earliest days of political activity he pledged himself to give his mind an idiom of pride and confidence that would reduce the flaw to a trifle. Every day he sought out a word he had never heard used before, the more majestic and recondite the better. That same evening he would march down to the Library and Institute and beat the local lads over the head with his new discovery.

It might have confused and infuriated the local lads, but it made Bevan one of the most brilliant verbal stylists in British political history. In this he can be compared with Churchill, his great antagonist, who also had a speech defect. Odd that the spokesmen of the two most maimed classes in our society, the over-privileged and the ghetto-people, should have been forced by the primitive communism of nature to share the same handicap.

Remember Churchill's remark that Bevan's first act under the new National Health Service should be to find its best psychiatrist and get himself treated. Clean, patrician fun, and Bevan himself revelled in the same kind of rich malevolence. He maintained the vigour of his hatreds for an unnaturally long time. In many politicians a kind of tactical schizophrenia sets in by the time they are forty. After that the right hand and the left lead totally separate lives, and the first hot inspirations of youth are served cold for supper.

But with Bevan one feels that what his immutably

radical friends would have called his mellowing duplicity, was simply an accident of late dusk. The fatigue of office and the onset of disease made him a little more averse to solitude and struggle.

Compared with him, Lloyd George used the escape apparatus early on. He found himself a war he could applaud in company with the dukes he had earlier wished to dynamite. Bevan had no such luck. The things he had identified as social blights as he walked the mining valley streets and made his first calculations, looked no less vile to him even after he had taken many hints of luxury and indulgence aboard his life, and lived in a house that had nothing of the Tredegar stamp.

Arthur Blessitt

Arthur Blessitt is a young American evangelist. He presents as odd a combination of gifts and qualities as any werewolf. If you can imagine Hughie Green crossed with Peter the Hermit you'll get the idea. 'Give me a J,' he shouts. The J is given. 'Give me an E,' and the E rolls back. In this simple way the name of Jesus is spelled out out and literacy, I take it, gains a little.

He tells stories of a sort rarely heard in pulpits. 'So there I was standing outside the porn shop with these Bibles under my coat. And to everybody who shuffled in I said, 'I've got a book here they don't dare to sell in there. And my Bibles went like hot cakes.'

He attributes part of his state of grace to being the son of a reformed drunkard and wife-beater, a powerful argument against drink and violence among parents. He travels up and down the country carrying a huge cross with a small wheel at the back to soften the more dolorous implications of the act. With a charming smile he stops in front of total strangers and says, 'Brother, share a prayer with me.' The smile vanishes and he prays, in a sincere and strangulated style suitable for this kind of intimate revivalism.

To many, this simple, homely zeal might bring great consolation, but there must be others for whom the encounter would involve nothing but a quick retreat to the tonic bottle or the padded room. Whatever Arthur's merits as a spirtual experience he makes a good performer. With or without the macabre burden he bears on his shoulder, Arthur will go, go, go far. We should welcome anything that defies the glacial advent of mental torpor in so many parts of the contemporary terrain.

Horatio Bottomley

Doomed cultures tend to be sensually exciting and extravagant. The days of Edward VII were no exception. A great swarm of peacocks, scamps and loons seemed to be having a wild pre-mortuary romp to give glitter to the post-Victorian epilogue. The world went into the trenches of its undoing with unbuttoned glee.

Horatio Bottomley was a minor but interesting twitch in an age of convulsions. Part benevolent crusader, part compulsive crook, he was a demagogue of genius. Whenever he patted the underdog the animal got a touch of rabies. He was also a con-man of imperial scope. He would leave a lavish tip, then purloin the dining table.

He shook a vengeful fist at the Establishment, promised every pauper a crown and feathered his own nest so amply there was scarcely a clothed bird in the land. If the juices of Santa Claus and Jack the Ripper could have been shaken into one terrible genetic cocktail, Bottomley might have been the result.

He cast a shadow over British politics which, in popular mythology, will never be completely lifted. He had gifts enough to furnish thirty rich careers, seduced enough women to worry or appease the suffragettes and replaced his blood-stream with champagne. In terms of abrasive repartee he was the Oscar Wilde of the workhouse. 'When my life is ended,' he said, 'three Horatios will glow from History's pages. Nelson, the one who held the bridge, and yours truly.'

Had he been the great admiral he would have stolen the navy. Had he been Horatius he would have sold the bridge to his own development company. As your truly his rise, fall and ruin satisfied every writer of improving moral tracts by going to gaol and dying a pauper. Plebian bilkers are, it would seem, allowed to go a limited way and are then put inside by larger, smoother predators who do not want too many of the hallowed institutions of theft dishonoured.

In his brief, post-prison twilight he made an appearance as a dying freak on a variety bill at the Windmill. He was still dreaming of climbing once again to the peaks of journalism and politics which he had once made his golden playground.

A man who had known him the days of his eminence saw him in gaol, working on mail-bags. Startled the man said, 'Hullo, Bottomley. Sewing?' 'No,' said the buccaneer, stabbing the canvas as if it were one of the High Court judges he loathd. 'Reaping.' At freedom he invariably breakfasted on champagne and kippers. Tea and cornflakes might have saved him or steadied him at least.

He made seventy eight thousand pounds from his recruiting speeches in World War One. Checking on the mortality figures on the Western Front, that must have worked out at about a shilling a death. If patriotism is the last refuge of the scoundrel, the other tenants of the refuge must have fled when Bottomley came in.

Charlie Chaplin

It is a striking fact that Charlie Chaplin's life was exactly the same compound of pathos, farce and tragedy as his comic art. The waves of adulation and hatred that alternately warmed and chilled his life were characteristic of a species and a society insanely searching for totems. He was the bard of painful surprise. He gave astonishment a new theatrical rhythm. The newly born cinema and his own personal style of comedy conveyed perfectly the restlessness of mankind hysterically on the move towards new hopes, doomed to harden into new brands of savage tyranny. He created scenes of rapturous irony and sadness that will last as long as the human eye. Disaster in Chaplin's comedies has a footwork nimbler even than Charlie's own.

Chaplin's art was one of the great contributions to the sad poetry of the uprooted. Even when, in old age, he faced that vast Hollywood throng baring its heart in shamed apology for America's virtual banishment of a staggeringly creative man, he still looked as if he was standing insecurely on the surface of an alien planet.

We are not likely to see many of his kind again. Television has planted a private cinema in every parlour and what, when Charlie started, was an electrifying novelty, has become a tedious commonplace. Comedians, committed within days of their first public utterance, to a weekly series, will rarely develop a comic image of any great depth. As for the content of Charlie's central myth, the lonely and forlorn will have no great appeal from now on.

King Farouk

The fact that a nation of starvelings should have accepted a man like Farouk as an omnipotent Pharaoh makes one want to order some new brand of tears. We can be thankful that he indulged in no worse vices than sex, gambling and duplicity, and did not saddle the world overlong with his presence.

After his coronation Farouk did not read a single book. He glanced though his State papers during short spells in the toilet and probably signified assent or rejection by a system of coded rattles on the chain. Monarch of a land whose labourers earned an average of ten pence a day, he lost fifty-five thousand pounds in an afternoon at Deauville on horses much brighter than himself. At a meeting of war-time leaders he smoked a cigar two inches longer than Churchill's and stooped a little forever after. He had to put up with a British High Commissioner who was seven feet tall and totally un-Egyptian.

Farouk was eternally frightened by men of authority and education, and as a King he kept bumping into them. The casino, brothel and a shameless obesity became his monasteries of refuge. It made one see his country as a place irreparably hurt by all the absurdities of which time is capable. Regal mummies with masks of gold in pyramids made by slaves will only land you in worse mischiefs. Egypt would have been well advised to hang on to Moses while it had him.

Josef Hermann

Josef Hermann is one of our most eloquent painters. Driven from his native Poland by pogroms, he escaped from the Nazis when they invaded Belgium by getting a lift in the car of an American lady called June Peach July. After the war he failed to trace her, probably because she had been compelled by the time's malignity to make a change of fruit and season.

He came to Ystradgynlais, in South Wales. 'On my first day there the evening sky over the valley had a copper tone. I stood near a stone bridge. A group of miners crossed the bridge and stood for a moment against the sunset. They were like figures on ikons. My mind has never shed the image'. He had grand things to say about his calling. 'There are some painters before whose technique I bow in deference. But there are others, the masters of humanity, Caravaggio, Rembrandt, Rouaux, before whom I tremble with the enthusiasm of love'.

I once visited Mr. Hermann in Ystradgynlais. His studio was in a room above a pub. In his customary mood of reckless effervescence he put me to sit on a deck-chair which he had been using as an improvised palette. I came away with enough paint on the seat of my trousers to have furnished the amiable genius with two more masterpieces.

Lord Home

'Panorama' had a profile of Lord Home. Since patrician statesmen should, logically, have vanished from our political map in 1914, we must salute him as an admirable anomaly. He has been blessed in his life and time. He has come through without experiencing two of the major blights of the modern world: serious intellectual brooding and worry about the roof over one's head. We saw him as a young M.P. representing, of all places, a constituency full of unemployed miners, leavened on his behalf by a residue of loyal serfs. One photograph showed him wearing a bowler so large no human face has ever appeared so small in relation to the hat above. Emblematic, perhaps, of a world growing too dark and overwhelming for the imagination of an Etonian cricketer.

The interviewer, in a mood of Jacobinical resolve, asked him 'What do you think when people say that you are a man of principle rather than principles?' Lord Home frowned, as if something odd had flown out of a spinney.

Then he asked with that hint of courteous impatience that comes from fourteen generations of privilege, peppered pheasants and riddled radicals, 'What exactly do you mean by that?' 'That you may be an honourable man who is not excessively clever.' Lord Home's reply was muttered and urbane, but somewhere in his mind must have floated the notion that a century ago such a piece of unholy impudence would have had the offender dangling in a feudal knot from some projecting bit of Border fortress.

A man of incomparable poise and a strong whiff of St. Fagans* who left one with the teasing suggestion that in the heather-scented paradise of his dreams, the poor, the black and red have not yet achieved any substantial identity.

*   Welsh Folk Museum near Cardiff

Roy Jenkins

Roy Jenkins is a politician of much more than average interest. He is without question the most untypical Welsh-man in sight. For more than one novelist in the future he will provide a field-day. His tastes and attitudes show a patrician fastidiousness light-miles removed from the min-ing valleys that produced him. His chosen area as a historian, the politics of the late Victorian and Edwardian times, and his temperamental choices, have led him to accept the Oxford of Rosebery and Asquith as the abiding home of the civilised imagination.

He has totally shed the diplomatic sentimentalities to which most Welsh people are prone. He is one of the few Welsh politicians who could resist the urge to remind his listeners that his father had been a miner, miners' agent and miners' M.P. The proletarian roots of the average tribune of the plebs would be openly enshrined. A statu-tory minimum of grammatical errors would be thrown in to reaffirm solidarity with the masses. Not so Mr. Jenkins. His accent and ideological style are impeccably Hampstead and country house.

Passionate concern with a separate and sacred Welsh identity he would dismiss as so much litter waiting to be tidied into history's bin. I recall him saying, 'I would possibly feel more at home in Madras than in Machyn-lleth,' and he put on what looked to me like an essentially Indian smile to underline the confidence of his supra-national self.

Father Joe

I would like to recall a most fascinating account of a priest known simply as Father Joe, a Catholic missionary who ministers to a vast slum of fragile shanties outside the Peruvian capital of Lima.

Father Joe is a tough American of Polish extraction. 'I wasn't all that bright in the seminary, so I made a vow that if I qualified I'd go and spend my life in any part of the world where the human suffering was unbearable'.

He has kept his vow. His huge and destitute parish of refugees from the hungry mountains behind Lima has grown like a leprous bark on the body of the city. Human fecundity in this context defeats reason and disgraces life. But while these aberrations still flourish and mankind fails to become properly and painlessly domesticated on this planet, let us be quietly thankful for the Father Joes who, with no pomp and not much pay, keep pity in motion and riven hearts assuaged.

Augustus John

John rampaged through life with all his appetites blazing and, as artist and lover, scaled peaks of splendour that left most of his contemporaries puritanically appalled or sourly envious. He was a bearded volcano, and from what I recall of some television interviews with him shortly before his death, he spoke in a ferocious rumble that had one ready to duck the lava. There is a story of John, brooding in a corner at some lively Chelsea shindig, startling the revellers by standing up and saying, 'Once I went to a party in Haverfordwest on a Thursday evening. It finished in Hungary the following Tuesday'. Ideologically, with his obsessive love for gypsies, he kept making that journey right through his life.

South Wales can have known few such flings. In the period which saw John's star glow over Europe, the average bit of social rejoicing of a licentious kind, rarely moved more than fifty yards further up the hill, where the air grew thin enough to ease the drink supply problem by making everybody giddy free of charge. There was an accident at Tenby in which John injured his head by diving on to an unexpected rock. He emerged from convalescence a genius in the Renaissance mould and a peacock of arrogant pride. Tenby Bay from now on will be full of bathers plunging fearlessly onto rocks, hoping to concuss themselves into supernormal talent.

Whether the intoxication came from erotic fury, champagne or bumps on the head, John's life was an inspired hangover. A plaque hangs in memory of him at Tenby. With typical Welsh deviousness, it was hung on the wrong house, unless the enormous span of his gifts spread his birth over three different dwellings.

Groucho Marx

The conversation between Groucho Marx and Frank Muir was a rich occasion. Groucho's is one of the dozen or so voices one might select to evoke the face and mood of the weird years that led us into the Second World War.

It is interesting that during the recent revival on television of almost all the Marx Brothers' films they found a vast and zealous following among younger viewers. Indeed, it is likely that the idol-smashing buffoonery that set the cinema of the thirties by the ears is more intelligible and appealing now than it was the first time round.

As the Brothers approached the end of their big creative period the world was setting its hand to lunacies that made the bizarre romps of Harpo and Chico and the radical savageries of Groucho seem as mildly sane as a magistrate's bench. Great comedians have an infallible way of prefiguring the monstrous. Give a king-sized jester a total freedom of expression and humanity will clutch its heart first in laughter, then in fear.

Watching Groucho with that other incomparable wit, Mr. Muir, it was fascinating to see how the snow of a weary kindliness had settled upon that volcano of sardonic wrath. I was reminded of three bachelor brothers who lived near my home when the Marx films began landing like shells in the valley stockades.

These men were withdrawn; they had drifted into Glamorgan from Cenarth, near Cardigan. They spoke a soft, purring kind of Welsh, designed not to upset coracles or alert water-bailiffs. They viewed talking pictures with a distrustful awe. They never ceased to ache for the safe tranquillity of Cenarth. The Rhondda they regarded as a catalogue of rate-paying outrages. The sounding cinema, as the Spaniards called it, struck them as just another antic of industrial man at his vilest.

I persuaded them to go and see 'Duck Soup', the third

of the Marx Brothers films. They were conservative in politics and the raking fire of Jacobinical irreverence from the screen drove them time and again to the cloister of the convenience. By the time we got to the anthem they were in a state of screaming confusion and had to be steered home. They wanted to charge the cinema manager with conspiracy to dement and defraud the Celt. But I persuaded them that legal action can often be even more inscrutable than the Marx Brothers. Never had the Atlantic of the spirit that separates the Teifi from the Bronx been so neatly bottled. Groucho in his eighties could still turn on a powerful beam. He explained that while his brothers remained virtually illiterate hedonists, he himself had tackled the intellectual Olympus the hard way. In his early days in burlesque he had read Anatole France in his dressing room, always with the door open. Because in the opaque ambience of American variety it is not enough simply to read Anatole France. One must be seen to be reading Anatole France.

And he gave a marvellous example of what one might call the acrobat's roll in verbal humour with which one fact can become a magnetic field for a host of cognate absurdities. 'Comedians pass their noon, wither and die, just like trees. Not Sir Herbert Tree. He came to Hollywood once to make a film. He pointed to the cameras and said, ''I can't act with those things standing there.'' He didn't understand that films can't be made without cameras. He must be dead now.' And by a magical twist of the voice, even death became just a subordinate joker, way down the bill.

Spike Milligan

The idea behind the series 'One Pair of Eyes' is very good. You ask a person to create a television essay on the thoughts, the objects, the dreams and obsessions around which his mind revolves. With a brief like that it would need an intractably dull man or woman indeed, to come up with a programme that did not have a glint or two of interest. It might, with perseverance, be possible to turn out a personal document in which nothing is communicated. But most of us have mental attics teeming with idiosyncratic elves eager to strut and fib about our hidden lives.

Most of the introspective pairs of eyes have given us sweeps of conventional autobiography. Which means that for some time past contributors have almost broken their necks to contrive something quirkier than the flat-footed sequence of 'I was born at . . .' 'My first success was . . .' 'I hope to die at . . .' The programme is God's gift to egomaniacs. I know. I have, in the plight of my time, been among the number.

In one edition, the subject was Spike Milligan, a brilliant, sad and utterly disturbing man. Having lived through many long public and personal nightmares he questions every facet of what the rest of us call reality. He shouts back at those elements of the grotesque and monstrous, pollution for profit, taxes and war, which most of us take in our staid submissive stride.

We saw him in Bayswater looking for the perfect doughnut. 'Last week you sold me one that was like lead with only a tiny bit of jam. You sent me another in a box. It was still like lead but there was a bit more jam.' He sounded like Blake experiencing a new apocalyptic flash.

He talked with an old street musician. 'Do you play requests? All right then. "Irish Eyes are Smiling."' And he sang lustily while the accordian played its muffled way through the ballad. Then he asked the old man if he had fought at the Battle of Mons. Yes, the veteran had so done. 'Did you see the Angel of Mons?' This was the legendary apparition that had flared out of the clouds above North-Eastern France, luminous, angelically feminine and firmly anti-German. The old man shook his head, No, he hadn't seen the Angel and clearly hinted that Spike should stick to musical requests.

The incident in the programme I shall most insistently recall showed us Spike with a blind heron. He has the aptitude of St. Francis for joyful pity and companionship in the presence of children and animals. The blind heron has a mate with a crippled wing. They have feelings of love but their mutilations deprive them of the skill and confidence needed to celebrate such affection.

Spike walked away from the heron, each of his eyes a blazing demand for a world of new miracles. A fascinating man, indeed, and the further he moves from his primitive goonery the more enriching he becomes.

Sir Oswald Mosley

There will always be something fascinating in the effrontery of any man who can come forward on a joint wave of vanity and wrath claiming that his will and inspiration can unite a divided nation, invigorate a sagging society.

One can have no complaints about Mosley's attitude to the established parties in the last great economic slump. There were too many weary men at Westminster, the best of their blood and talent already shed in battles long since won or lost. They wished only for quietness in the garden of self-satisfaction where they sat watering their inward bankruptcies.

But Sir Oswald was not the man to topple them. His models, Hitler and Mussolini, had the stamp and the scream of the slum about them. Your true demon will never come from a country house. The great demagogue must never have been weakened by the cocktail and croquet set. The man who wants to storm and flatten the citadels of the Establishment, must come to it, as the mob does, from the outside, as a stranger, a lout who can hammer the fears and greeds of the less informed into the shape of a gun.

Evan Roberts

Few writers exposed to the more powerful myths of South Wales life, can fail to be attracted by the name and mystery of Evan Roberts, the evangelist. He still rattles about inside the sounding shell of our experience. He came roaring out of the West, his own conscience on fire, and left a multitude of minds charred and astonished.

The atmosphere of the times must have been charged with a sense of cataclysm. Coal was reaching its productive peak. Not a seam was to be left unripped. Mines could be gutted by flame, villages decimated by death. To live with an angry roughness took some pain from part of the outrage. The valleys brimmed with hopes and dreads, longing for a focus. The great agitators of the colliers' union provided it in part.

But for many, especially the women, the Messenger, in the Mohammedan sense of the term, would need a wider field of reference than coal or politics. It was the whole tormenting storm of sin, despair, God's angels opting for cloth-capped squalor, that needed to be challenged and purged. A large, hastily assembled and vigorously abused world was lifting its sad sails to catch the wind of a little restitution.

Evan Roberts was the wind that came, and like the wind he went. He chose a dangerous and impossible task but he made it brief, and in that fact alone, the swift landing and passage of a bilingual, simple-minded meteorite, our endless curiosity is rooted. He was like all dynamic South Wales talents, a fugitive from pit-labour and neurosis, and having ignited a large tract of Welsh sensibility sidled off to a retreat in that most stolidly English of places, Derbyshire.

A.L. Rowse

Most minds keep looking back for traces of some vanished light, some smiling corner of time, a glade of serenity and goodness, where no rough winds rise to rip our illusions into rags. Historians are lucky people in this respect. They have the tools to bore a deep hole in the fabric of our yesterdays and use it as a cavern of joyful calm while our contemporary squalls blow over.

Take the distinguished scholar A.L. Rowse. He was born of poor parents in Cornwall. He won a scholarship to one of the world's resplendent colleges, Christ Church, Oxford, the creation of that most sumptuous of racketeers, Cardinal Wolsey. There he took the time of Elizabeth I as his domain and has become as potent a courtier of the great Queen as Essex or Raleigh ever were.

The present age he regards as merely the most violent spasm in the long decline of what he sees as a unique moment of virility, wit and grace in the history of England. His shrine is the memory of a Britain in the first morning of her Protestant passion and the great bull's rush of inspired piracy. His mental exile from the twentieth century Welfare State murk, he has made official by going to live in a Cornish mansion that brings to mind the squires who rushed to horse and ship at the first glare of the beacons that told us the Armada was on its way up Channel. He said he regards himself as one of the luckiest men alive. I back his opinion.

Jimmy Savile

I understand that many people sustain their evening's viewing with a series of quick snacks. The mind, beneath a steady fall of cheese, bread, pickles and liquid opiates, remains snugly unresponsive to the drift of images across the screen that would, given their head, take the conscience to some California of clear conviction.

I don't blame them for seeking visas to torpor land. Not all the religions of the world have treated mankind to such a pitiless ration of terror, pity and wrath as the average television week. I can't see how any one can emerge from a bout of sustained viewing with the sure feeling that one is a complete and significant personality. The bombarded eye can only take in the impression of a mass of human identities mashed beyond any possibility of precise definition. We exist only as symptoms, and they are never too clear, never too encouraging.

Take Jimmy Savile. There is a symptom of vigorous confusion if ever there was one. In "The World of Jimmy Savile" he spoke to us directly and the experience was weirdly enlightening. He is the Pied Piper of Hamelin that has no sincere desire to be rid of its plague. We saw him laying his priestly spell in the temple of Pop. He demonstrated his great strength cycling across Britain for charity.

He loves being seen by people and is so enchanted by the progress of his own fulfilment that there are now Messianic hints in his message. We saw him standing before a zealous multitude, stripping off his garments and distributing them among the believers. He can say things that bring the scoffer up short. "I don't look any funnier now than I did when I came out of the pit after a day's work. I wasn't ashamed then. I'm not ashamed now."

Of his work as a comforter of the sick, a doctor said, 'After forty years in this profession, if that man's a phoney, I'll quit medicine.' Mr. Savile tried his hand at theology and did rather less well than he does on his cycle. 'My God is a good guy, great sense of humour.' I would like to submit that phrase to St. Paul, Cotton Mather, the witchburner of Salem, Massachusetts and Tom Stenner, a miner who worked to a less ambitious fuel-target than Mather and merely singed the ferns of the Lower Rhondda with his fits of apostolic rage.

I would like to submit those seers to a saliva test after hearing the message according to St. Jimmy. All the same there is a hunger in the souls of men and Jimmy Savile is the morsel that gives it comfort. Never have the needy sheep, expecting food, had to alter so little the angle of the expectant neck.

Leslie Stuart

Our thousands of popular songs have been life-savers for the millions of people with nothing much to say. They are the instant magic spells for those with no other access to sorcery. By the simple murmuring of their lyrics, hearts have been won by men not meant by society or nature to be much use as lovers.

Songs that are easy to hum have done more to lubricate life and send it rolling along pleasant paths than any number of speeches or machines. A simple ballad can do more to tranquillise people than an aspirin or a bludgeon.

I once knew a man who told me that when he was no more than sixteen he had great success with girls by going straight up to them, tipping his first adult hat, a bowler, and singing archly a song called, 'Tell Me, Pretty Maiden, Are There Any More At Home Like You?' This worked like a charm until the father of one of the girls, a man out of tune with life and love, cut off from hedonism and the top twenty, stepped out of the shadow and caught him a clip that sent him down the street, reeling and singing 'Soldiers of the Queen', hoping to catch the father on his patriotic side.

Leslie Stuart wrote five or six truly pervasive songs that have become a rib of our popular culture in the last hundred years. Anyone who claims to have gone through life without singing, whistling or humming one of the tunes from 'Floradora' should be invited to come in for a warm.

Stuart's life was music from start to finish. His father kept a pub in Manchester called 'The Slip Inn'. When Stuart was nine the pub pianist collapsed and died over the keyboard. He was removed and instantly replaced by the young lad and the concert went on. If ever I am looking for an image to describe an audience really intent on a sing-song, I shall think of those patrons of ''The Slip Inn''.

Stuart went on to write songs for Eugene Stratton, an American song-and-dance man who blackened his face, a pioneer version of Al Jolson. Between them they gave the world 'Lily of Laguna' and the world still has it. Both men were tireless gamblers and had their last quarrel and parted for ever at Hurst Park, a place where horses ran and men grew crotchetty.

Stuart's experience as a church-organist in the first half of his life made him ambitiously eager for an acclaim more solemn than the beery bravos of the music-hall. At his death he left an opera 'Nina'. It was unpublished, unperformed. Today, fifty years later, it is in exactly the same state. I don't think he would have needed to fret. It is enough to have been the mouthpiece of the bawling ecstasies of millions. You know the lovely story of Cyrano de Bergerac. The songwriter is oddly in that same kind of pathetic fix.

Alf Garnett is the patron saint of the mentally unfurnished and physically uncouth, while nourishing the self-conceit of a dandy and philosopher king. In his arrogance and timidity he is the Hamlet of the sawdust bar, lord of the collarless flannel shirt and conveyor-belt drinking, his life an endless flow of pints and idiocies.

As an infant howls out of an empty stomach, victim of a vocational discomfort, Alf howls out of an empty mind. He is the fear-crazed guardian at the mouth of the tribal caves, shooing away the new monsters of experiment and change.

*

Lloyd George, coming out of a dusty nowhere enriched by a compost of peasant genius, transformed most of our social reflexes and picked up the world's most formidable ruling class by its indifferent ears.

*

I have heard it said that some choristers become sexually disabled as the result of vocal excess.

*

In a programme on censorship I was struck by the fact that the antipornographers seem to get a merrier time of it than the rather melancholy people who watch, read or peddle the stuff. The perverts may be on the wrong horse. My favourite among the moralists was a lady who had not seen 'Last Tango' but wanted all films banned on principle. If the fuel crisis deepens, the poor old witches will be burning again.

If Britain Had Fallen

'If Britain Had Fallen' left one with many thoughts: It is an abuse of imagination to attribute to the Germans horrors additional to the ones they actually did. They worked hard at being monsters and their total achievement, nakedly shown, is quite enough. They did a unique disservice to humanity and we have sentenced them to behave impeccably for the next thousand years. They have the right to appeal and probably will.

If their criminal delirium (from 1933 - 45) stemmed from some traditional blood-clot on their collective mind, the clot has been thinned and partly removed by time and considerate foes. We wish them a happy convalescence, wryly reflecting that in the history of the world there has never been a more expensive bit of therapy laid on for a gaggle of tribal idiots.

I have a feeling that the moon until quite recently was a flowering and sensitive planet. Having a good view of the earth and Hitler, it lost all wish to remain a sentient part of the solar system and became the ashen and indifferent lump we now know it to be.

The film suggested that Britain might have been smashed into submission, to become a more or less compliant 'gau' within the Reich. I'm not sure. There is an element of crazy, wolfish pride in the British character that might well have bitten and shaken the life out of even those psychopathic freaks. There would have been more than a touch of the Viking's funeral about our resistance. And Hereward the Wake, with American money and backed by a suspension of our best-loved hobby, the classwar, would always be a good bet.

All the same the programme kept up a fine flow of shocks and revelations. There were fascinating probes by Lord Chalfont into the minds of odd survivors. And the usual crop of grating exposures. In the occupied Channel

Islands some people spoke of having been served orders of deportation to the Continent, there to work and almost certainly to die, as slave labourers. These orders in the case of a few were cancelled and they arrived back at their homes within two hours to find every scrap of their furniture and clothes looted and gone. The offenders were not Germans but their neighbours. When the tiger has a brainstorm the mice go mad as well.

I can imagine a smug German historian, fifty years from now, writing many a laughing footnote on the vileness of some of the defeated during the years when the Nazis were riding their high, homicidal wave.

Personal memories were the most bearable reaction to theories of what might have happened during that ghastly September of 1940. One remembers phases of moonlight so lovely and made lovelier by the thought that we might shortly be running out of moon. We all waited for the church bells that would ring to tell us the Germans were here, marching or floating.

A vicar near us broke under the tension. He started seeing huge white spots in front of his eyes that grew to monstrous size with the deepening of his panic. Then the spots started to show German markings and in no time he was in the belfry, his cracking mind in a universe of hostile parachutes, giving his bell-rope a series of magisterial tugs that filled every local ditch with terrified citizens and eager militiamen.

I found myself wondering how Wales would have fared if the Germans had taken us over. Badly, I would say. Our long tradition of radical dissent and humanitarian evangelism would have made us sure targets for the cemetery list or some purgatorial camp in one of our emptier valleys. There would have been areas of strong anti-English bias that would have puzzled Hitler a bit, and the vampirical Himmler, while deaf to the merits of penillion, might for a moment have been impressed by the fact that a Welshman had pioneered cremation in Western Europe.

But our reprieve would have been brief, mainly because of the second private language in which our loathing of Germans, lumped with the Normans, and weekend cottagers, could have been expressed. That would, in Nazi eyes, have been the unforgiveable sin. We would, with the exception of the odd few enthusiasts waiting in a cave for King Arthur's return, have gone the dark way of the Hungarian gypsies and the Jews of everywhere south of Dover.

There is a nice marginal note to all this. In the late nineteen forties Humphrey Jennings wished to make a film about Lidice, the town destroyed by the Nazis as a reprisal for the murder of Heydrich, the S.S. chief in Czechoslavakia. The men of Lidice, old and young, were killed, the women enslaved, their houses burned.

For his location Jennings chose Gwaen-cae-Gurwen and among the fierce-faced resisters and martyrs in the film were Dai Dan Evans and Dai Francis, miners' leaders and militants who would, had the curse come to our doors, have shown no mercy to the philosophers of race and blood, and would, as congenital anti-fascists, have been shown no mercy. Another black-draped chair to mark and mourn the death of all poetry would have saddened the Eisteddfod stage, and Wales would at last have given up its restless ghost. The Nazis could have grown so tired of deciding who not to kill in this nonconformist patch of ours, they might even have gone home to renew themselves at the lunatic shrines of Nuremberg.

The shape and sound of the self you eventually become depend on a number of more or less perverse things. There is the pace of the cash-flow, the strength of the sunlight and the incidence of laughter within the years of child-hood. There is the quirky conduct of the glands which so frequently mislead their owner's intentions. But above all, in putting the final touches to the model we put in the shop window as the last, definitive article of identity, we must acknowledge the power of the stories that we take in on our walk through life. We respond endlessly to strokes of other people's imaginations that get below the skin and colour and flavour every inch of our bloodstream. A man at ninety is still playing tricks of wishful magic he read about in tattered volumes he raced through in rapture at the age of nine.

*

With the Industrial Revolution in Britain entering into a critical phase of shrinkage and failure, it might be better to start picking through the debris of the system that created our first cotton mills, shipyards and steelworks for clues to whatever secrets of energy and optimism drove those peo-ple forward. Serious thought about our current experience is going to disinfect many of the loathsome bogeys of the eighteenth and nineteenth centuries. We might even see an advertisement in *The Times* asking Satan to turn up as a possible adviser to the Secretary of State for Employ-ment.

GWYN THOMAS

The Sexual Cease-Fire

In a time when so many grievances are becoming explosive and blowing bits off our slender fabric of sanity, let us make haste to stop the simmering resentment that separates the sexes. Anyone who now goes out of his way to hinder the full emancipation of women should be threatened with a writ for high treason.

Sexual inequality, in the hands of ruthless employers, is an abominable fraud, and in the mouths and literature of the Women's Liberationists, an absolute bore. Let's have done with it. If gainful work is done, either it is done by a machine or a human being. Not by a man as distinct from a woman.

It is woeful that at this stage of the 20th century women should have to talk of their female status in the same piercing mood of indignity as Shylock used to describe his identity as a Jew.

The plague of the human mind at the moment is sour resentment about ancient grievances. They are overdue for the boneyard. The suffragettes have been crying in the wilderness for far too long. Their voices tend to be over-pitched and wearying on the tympanum. They need a rest. Of course, the male chauvinist will say that the wilderness in which most women sing out for greater freedom has always been a bit of a rest-home, but male chauvinists, by any standard, have become the least rational members of a never too lucid species.

Over the last decades sexual divisions have taken some fair knocks. The whole business of sexual relationships has been shaken more briskly than a cocktail. If there were a dyspeptic and gloomy seer like Thomas Carlyle still on the premises, he would have much to say on the subject. But since a latter-day Carlyle, with his thunderous pessimism, would by now have been killed or cured by the flippancy that has ousted all other opiates off the market, I will sit on

Carlyle's mummified knee and do an Archie Andrews, a ventriloquial stint, on his behalf.

The lines between the sexes have grown fainter and we have had brigades from both camps outside with scrubbing brushes to make the boundaries fainter. The formal marital alliances that have defined women's status in the past have become ricketty. They have developed leaks in the roof and bad subsidence at the bottom. The whole business of setting up a home has become maddeningly difficult. Prices are making the old domestic ritual like the Sunday roast as insubstantial as a mirage.

With the mortgages becoming steeper than the Himalayas, and pork chops as rare and dear as uranium, it is possible to prophesy that wedlock will shortly be replaced by a loosely organised promiscuity, and the traditional family homestead by a corner in a youth-hostel, with the youths touching ninety and wearing shorts, not because they wish to suggest an abiding enthusiasm for fitness, but because they cannot afford the rest of the trousers.

Vegetarianism and free love will grow like sunflowers and by the century's end meat and marriage will be over the hill. A whole new generation of debt poisoned hedonists will pause on their way to gaol or the psychiatric ward, only to choose swiftly between a new mistress and a munch of melon.

It will be good when all the stupid, artificial barriers are down, and men and women can clearly see what goes on in their own backyards. Men are bitterly convinced that women, while less able than themselves, are having a whale of a time on their backs, on men's backs, of course. Women are certain that men are a shiftless lot who would, without the stimulus of women's love and drive, paternal affection and family responsibilities, lapse into a torpor and drop out of the whole game of human evolution.

A woman whose intense convictions I never fail to respect, once told me that she could never set eyes on a man without seeing a gorilla, and she would cause a little social confusion by throwing him a nut and a banana and helping him on to the nearest branch.

Whole mythologies of hatred and mistrust have grown in the neutral but increasingly disturbed land between the sexes. When such things as pay discriminations are cleared away, then for the first time we can be frank about the legendary indictments of men by women and of women by men that make up ninety-five per cent of our folk-lore and gossip. Each suspects the other of inhabiting wonderlands of vice and indulgence. Men suspect women of a rabid concern with appearance, allure, the whole sorceer's kitchen of the cosmetics industry and the raving asylum of the fashion trade.

We must learn to understand that a concern with physical beauty is not simply a witless sexual ploy designed to inflame innocent men at their grass-cutting, and to make them throw down their mowers from hands hot with desire, every time Cleopatra Williams passes down the street with a new rainbow of art and delight in her mint-fresh coiffure and sculpted trouser suit. Men, when they are no longer better than women, may have to learn the average woman's anguish at having to choose between four different hair-stylists, all dedicated, in her view, to malicious incompetence and doing far more for other women than for herself.

And many women in the rougher, more honest air of parity, will learn that the ideal of sexual magnetism has become irrelevant. They will forget that life is not a perpetual screen-test and that the lights of world attention do not switch on every time they step through the front door. Thousands of male psychotics stand in their unhappy twilight because of the length of time women take getting ready, the agony of finding fifteen drinking minutes sagging into ninety minutes of watching the television rolling its peculiar eyes, while the last touch of loveliness is being applied in the bedroom.

And women will learn, too, that men's lives are not a

private clubland of licentious ease. They will be asked, on the new plateau of equality, to partake in a few beer-logged sessions at the domino and crib tables in the bottom-priced bars, the evening muffled in a tidal flow of flat ale and moronic muttering about horses and foot-ballers.

It might cause them to pass a vote of no confidence in the sisters Pankhurst and generations of crusaders who have lamented underprivilege and proclaimed their envious hatred of men. Most of us do not deserve love. None of us deserve hatred. We are all doing the best we can with faulty raw materials.

The more the world's house shakes, the more reverently we look at the fixed stars in the sky, the beloved things that were there yesterday and will be there tomorrow.

*

To allow anything of grace and beauty from the past to perish without protest, or an effort to defend, is the blackest treason. The only gesture of consolation we can offer the dead victims of injustice is to cherish the few great works of talent that grew from the workings of inequality and its odd, occasional by-product, great flashes of aesthetic insight and zeal.

*

There is nothing so pleasant as the sight of a fulfilled personality, a person whose inward dreams have ticked away happily in rhythm with the world and the mood of their times.

*

The whole dilemma of living is summed up in the differing view of cats held by mice and lonely old ladies.

*

She revealed a talent for nymphomania that caused all the cocktail glasses in Chelsea to be raised in her honour.

Crown of Privilege

Who are the luckiest people you know? Answers to that question would give you a map of our society's envies and its dreams. Some would say that the most fully blessed among us are pop-stars, racehorse owners, oil-tycoons or promoters of strip-shows. Others, more cautious and sceptical, would opt for the dead. But the more thoughtful, in all probability, would put their money on University dons.

For most of us, these sheltered scholars wear a special crown of privilege. They can lead lives of meditative calm. They can rest their heads on the pillow of a deeply-rooted culture. Upheavals among the student body are mild and soon assuaged. The kind of rattling cataclysms currently shaking the teeth out of trades like coal and steel they are never likely to know.

For the rest of this century at least they will spend their days in beautiful, bookish insulation, the last heirs of what one may call the respectful dialogue of civilisation. The barbarian in their constant nightmare is an insolent lout making uneconomic demands in ungrammatical English and burning a bookshop to get warm on a cold soccer afternoon.

So, as the noise of chaos thickens, it is interesting to find out how much of the vulgar rumpus is getting through the walls of their ivory towers, and how our senior sages feel about the gales currently blowing our serenity to tatters.

I once heard Harold Wilson speak about the thinkers who sit around the High Tables of Oxford and Cambridge. He implied that an excess of port, leisure and detachment from the rabble had given them an unnatural taste for forecasts of doom.

They become convinced that the lucky fluke which has provided their own personal good fortune cannot possibly extend to a whole society. So their thoughts make a pleasant nightly tour of such places as Atlantis, and Pompeii, which thought they were on to a good thing then suddenly found they were wrong.

'There are dons at Oxford,' said Harold Wilson, 'who haven't yet forgiven Britain for defeating the Spanish Armada.'

Sundays have always bewildered me. A large part of the floor of my mind is made up of those marathon stints of piety that were the cultural paving stones of a Rhondda boyhood. Even now the Sabbath catches me in alternating postures of enthusiasm, alarm and sadness. But certain forms of religious programmes I cannot resist. Welsh hymn singing. Hearing it, I walk again among all those loved and loving people who gave warmth and beauty to the first years of my pilgrimage.

*

The Welsh have always been partial to cheese and forecasts of doom. In my native valley we had a patriarchal neighbour who, through mouthfuls of roasted Cheddar, gave us regular news of the world's impending end. The time, the details. He gave us the lot. Luckily for our sanity he was a noisy eater and we missed half of what he said. The old man was also convinced that the lowering prophet Jeremiah was Welsh, with the surname Jones. If ever he was tempted to be hopeful about man's future, a bite of cheese put him right back on his path of blissful desperation.

Ballet

One Bank Holiday Monday, seeking some maypole mood of wanton gaiety, I switched on to 'Tales of Beatrix Potter'. I gazed at it with an expression as grey as the perfidious weather which rushes into service as soon as the news gets around that the British have a day off work and are in a mood to romp.

The societies with which I have been acquainted have moved with a heaviness of gait that did nothing to prepare me for the intense daintiness of ballet. In my book, people who lift their legs high in the air have just stepped in something. As for nursery tales, the most light-hearted anecdotes dished out to us in the kitchens of my childhood featured Sodom, Gomorrah and Jezebel, the first two burned, the third stoned, and how it served them right.

I envy people who love ballet and can dispense periodically with the torment of words. I also envy people who can cherish through a whole lifetime the sort of fable that Miss Potter wrote.

There must be many Britons who have tripped through life insulated from the grosser brands of reality through having learned by heart in infancy the winsome doings of Mrs. Piggy-Winkle, Jemima Twitchit and Squirrel Nutkin.

When money first knocked on the human door it sprang a lethal trap. Humanity's neck broke. That explains the funny look you see on its face before, during and after Christmas.

*

When inadequacy becomes rhetorical and revenges itself on years of neglect and humiliation, watch out, and wear your bullet-proof waistcoat.

*

There is no prayer long enough to express all we would like to say about the need for mercy on our souls.

*

I don't know whether you've looked lately, but there's something peculiar about the mind of modern man.

*

Mr. Aspinall, a friend of Lord Lucan, the errant earl— 'Friendship and loyalty are my only religion. If Lucan were a fugitive here I should never betray him'. People whose moral sense has been numbed by gambling will applaud him. Nannies who stand to be clubbed to death by deranged aristocratic employers will have reservations.

Sob Sisters

If it had escaped our attention before, television would have long since rubbed our callous noses into the fact that the one crop that needs no help from fertiliser is distress. We are good at it. We are all acrobats at the job of tying our minds and bodies into knots. Most lives have a jet-stream of anguish bringing up the rear. Open any office of consolation, in the name of religion or medicine, and you will find a queue outside trailing wounds and perplexities for treatment and solution.

The Agony Column has for decades been a flourishing feature of newspapers. Sob-sisters achieve the status of Sibyls as they dish out their daily answers to anything from broken hearts to moulting budgies and cases of a dray-man's droop. Nothing floors these menders of shattered lives. 'Once, on a sloping roof I received a strange sugges-tion from my Uncle Duncan. Ever since then I have been frightened of heights. What should I do?' Like a flash the sting gets its dab of ointment. 'Dear Harassed. Find a flat roof or shoot your Uncle Duncan.'

Most dilemmas are so outrageous or irremediable that it is better to see them dealt with in print. In that form they can be embraced in seconds, given their ration of moral concern, pity or contempt and dismissed.

But on television, with the victim and counsellors in plain view the problems grow on you. The world seems to fill with worry and disquietude and one despairs of ever again meeting a normally contented person. And there is a carking belief that for some people getting into trouble is a skill like throwing darts or playing the banjo.

In 'Let's Talk It Over' the applicant for advice sat in a shadow which was thoroughly disturbing even before the chronicle of frustrations and fears began. It was perfectly suggestive of a person trapped beyond redemption, and one felt that as soon as the present fix was resolved the victim would nip out at once and find another.

The grievances were laid out before Dr. Wendy Green-gross and two aides. They were seasoned comforters and trouble-shooters. Dr. Greengross had a way of nodding the head which was in itself a great psalm of assuagement. No smiles, nothing as shallow or facile as that. Just that marvellous nodding, a pulse of understanding and pity.

I would hate to be a problem exposed to such bright beams of percipience as come from this trio of oracles. Even more would I hate to be the owner and confessor of that problem. As too many cooks are said to spoil the broth, too many lighthouses may spoil the wreck. There's a lot to be said for choosing your emotional mishaps with care, ordering them in special flavours and learning, with wry resolution, to enjoy them. 'Let's Talk It Over' was a hard programme to escape from. Despair is magnetic and when tears blur the eyes it is difficult to find the switch.

⌘

It is a mark of our time that more and more people step into the spotlight of world fame at an absurdly early age. Some of them make it so young that at thirty they are already senile anachronisms.

*

When children ape adults even the apes complain.

Hadrian's Wall

In Hunter Davies' admirable documentary on Hadrian's Wall he approached two young workers who looked as if they devoted what time they had off from scholarship to the pursuit of ale and soccer frenzy. 'Where does Hadrian's Wall begin?' he asked one, 'Search me,' came the neat reply. 'What do you know about the Roman Wall?' he asked the other who must have sneaked a look at the handbook. 'The Romans built it,' he said. An angry farmer, sick of having archaeologists and tourists poking cultural and curious noses into his fastness, said, 'My cows come first. The Roman Empire comes last.'

Lovely facts tinkled like ice in the glass of remembered time. General Wade looted the Wall to make military roads after Culloden. Hadrian would have liked that. He would have had no time for the lightweight Bonnie Prince Charlie or the freelance skullduggery of the clans. As popular interest in archaeology spreads, the feet of trippers marching on the Wall are likely to do more damage than two thousand years of time and erosion. Hadrian could not have liked that. He deplored trippers. When he left home he was in no hurry to get back and wherever he went he paid the bill in lasting stone.

England's North East has a vast vitality. Elastic principles of public stewardship rub broad shoulders with sheepdogs of University standard and memories of ancient conflict in a landscape now utterly calm and rich.

I did not know Hadrian but I once fell off his Wall. I was asked, some summers ago, to take part in a television series on the treasures of the British Museum. I was happy to be drawn into this pool of glittering antiquities. Someone had heard me make a bitterly abusive remark about racketeering usurers in imperial Rome and what they did obliquely to the daughters of Boadicea.

So, on a June morning I found myself standing on the great rampart speaking to camera about the disparate rhythms of resentment that cause the deprived to rush screaming at the throats of the secure. They thought, with charity and courage that I was the man to interpret the Romano-British age for the small screen. My words must have touched the nerve of some sleeping wrath. A wind of freakish violence swept down from Caledonia. A stone slipped beneath my feet. I was already giddy from talking off the cuff five feet above the ground and I landed on my back on the southern side of the barrier. The camera crew brushed me down while I explained to Hadrian that the barbarians, with their gift of sullen mischief, must still be around.

In the ecstacy of resolving a quadratic equation, Archimedes failed to hear the footsteps of the men who had come to kill him. Equations never got that hold on me. The last time I tried to tackle an equation in a classroom, the master bludgeoned me with an ebony ruler. I heard every detail as clear as a bell.

*

Teachers, at every level of human activity, have never gone out to bat on a gloomier wicket.

A Creative Inquiry

In a world that changes with pantomime speed few things have altered more than the teaching of geography. Once it was a crude and simple affair. There were oceans, there were mountains. If you knew the difference between wet and dry, steep and flat, you were home. In the dawn of my learning life, I recall a teacher of geography. The school was poorly equipped. There was such a lack of visual aids the headmaster thrashed us with a white stick to make the cultural famine official. The teacher ran a little private tuck-shop, selling lollies of a modest kind to the richer scholars in the break.

With the profits he bought a globe. It had a heavy iron base and he carried it proudly up and down the corridors, sagging under the strain. At first we thought it was a publicity ploy connected with his tuck-shop operation, and we took the globe to be a king-sized gob-stopper or humbug.

Today the thunderbolts of communication have involved us with the face and feel of the planet. Let some evil befall the North Pole or the tropics and we have a shrewd and instant sense of where and how the people are grieving. If we still used a watch-chain we'd be wearing the world on it, our personal bauble. Thanks to the invasion of our lives by moving pictures, the continents have become extra rooms in a private house.

Geography has become an examination of the plight of people. Conventional history teaching was once an inquest into the crises of the past. Geography is now very largely a creative inquiry into the errors of the present. Fools wishing to tip us into some new dilemma will never feel as safe and confident again. People taking Human Studies courses will be on to them like a shot. Consider an item in the geography syllabus of that marvellous educational venture, the Open University. It dealt with the problem of derelict mining villages in Durham. A generation ago the plague of uselessness could beset huge areas and no one except those immediately hurt would give the pip of a damn. Pain was normal, people were patient, rogues had a ball.

Today we are aware of the living tissue involved in every human situation. The price and profitability of coal still greatly matter, but the men who mine it, and get the less lovely end of the social stick in so doing, have a new edge of meaning. They are still a bit behind the dukes, but the race is beginning to look slightly less ridiculous. We saw maps of Durham at the turn of the century literally pitted with dots showing active collieries, and fever-spots of industrial vigour.

Today only a few collieries remain. Villages for which there is no hope of revival are served with a Schedule D notice. D for Dead, Dispersal, Demolition. Chilling, but whole worlds better than the torpor of indifference that attended bitter social changes in the past.

The Scots lose their teeth faster than any other community on earth. From the onset of puberty it seems, their gums long for nudity. If they don't lose their teeth from an intake of excessive sugar, they go along to the Celtic-Rangers match and get them knocked out.

*

Animals must often marvel at our ways of making a living. When they got an eyeful of wrestling they must have extended the period of hibernation. I am grateful for my childhood's immersion in an ethic that regarded grappling with men, for whatever reason, as deplorable.

*

Truculence has become the keynote of most contemporary intercourse. So many attitudes are hardening, they are giving life its most calloused look to date. So many people are digging their heels in, it is becoming almost a branch for farming.

In Need of Forgiveness

Despite many centuries of hard Christian effort, forgiveness as a practical concept still does not have many takers. For great numbers, the thought and act of punishment promote a stronger sensual excitement than preparing for and making love. A dream fixed in innumerable minds is a world swept clean by storms of vengeance of all their enemies.

These irascible fanciers of revenge have had to be cured by incessant propaganda and legislation. Over the last hundred years the human individual has been made a great deal safer from the scourge of murderous censors and tyrants. With even the most infuriating pests we accept the duty of patience and the prospect of low returns on our investment of mercy.

But those who regard mankind as a mob of monstrous offenders badly in need of periodical weeding and whipping remain a powerful lobby. You can spot their eyes in crowds if you watch closely. They are dark with charred disgust at what they consider our society's inept and cowardly surrender to the forces of decadence and treachery.

They dream hungrily of the time when morality showed no trace of rickets and walked with the deadly assurance of a gunfighter within a safe, walled city for the greater happiness of the walled classes.

These activists would have a ball if they considered Charlemagne. He was the Frankish King who tried to restore a sense of political coherence into a Europe gone daft with disorder when the Empire founded by Augustus and Claudius had fallen apart some four hundred years before. Civic institutions had rotted away. Invasions of savage pagans throbbed in from the East at short intervals and strode to victory, up to their sword-belts in lapsed insurance policies.

Barbarism was the disease of the age. Clement and

compassionate reformers, when they managed to arise at all, waxed briefly, addressed a deaf world and vanished into the general darkness of villainy. The man who would hammer the stamp of a new identity would need a jocular imagination and a fluent addiction to violence. It would need a man like Charlemagne.

To kill a thousand men to make a single point was easy for him. And expedient, of course. After all Europe still had six centuries to wait before the printing press came into being and news was hard to circulate without the help of emphatic gestures.

It is just as well that the European leaders who now wear the Charlemagne Medal, struck to honour those who helped to found and extend the E.E.C., use golf-clubs instead of swords. I can imagine what Charlemagne would do to the people now griping daily about the Common Agricultural Policy. 'I've mislaid my sword but drown these varlets in the wine lake.'

From ancient barbarians to Yahoos of newer vintage, the urban hooligan of today. If, in some final bout of exasperation with smashed windows, despoiled telephone boxes and bus-stops, we should bring back the birch, we must be sure that the thongs will land on the right shoulders.

Dehumanise a landscape and you will get a less than human response from the people in it. The guilt of planners who rip out the organic warmth of old communities and replace them with high-rise tower blocks cannot be assessed. With a vast, implicit hooliganism poisoning the power-flow in greedy and fearful societies, you cannot expect that the bored and idle ruffian at the corner will, at the drop of an episcopal oration, donate his cash to Oxfam and slip on a halo.

When nations fall below the natural levels of creative vigour and simple honesty, you can expect the young to reflect that fact exactly. We have done monstrous evil with the very best intentions. Slum clearance without clear regard for the fragility of goodness in urban areas is a classic instance of pouring out the baby with the bath water. We have altered the tone of dereliction, little more.

A Reflection On De Gaulle's Funeral

It took a strong arm of annihilation to remove Charles de Gaulle. The Notre Dame scene was dazzling, so operatic in its lighting and grouping, one expected to hear an Anvil Chorus come in to give extra body to the Bach Chorale. The eye fed eagerly on Pompidou's face, fastidious, slightly fearful, as if anxious that the too great man might change his mind. On Mr. Heath, also, wearing an air of sharp intelligence, looking around as if seeking ways to modernise the whole mechanism of piety. On Mr. Nixon's bodyguard, looking at the whole world with acute suspicion, viewing the surrounding dignitaries, Haile Selassie, Mrs. Gandhi, the Shah of Persia, as if they were all potential gunmen and assassins. At the village funeral we heard 'Nearer My God To Thee' sung in French. In my childhood we heard this hymn sung at so many funerals we thought it was part of the coroner's clearance to go ahead. Heard at the General's passing it gave the whole thing an ineffable homeliness.

Any species is suspect that needs to remind itself annually with such deafening emphasis that kindliness is an indispensable element in life. It is little wonder that tradition has Santa Claus approach the human scene heavily disguised and at dead of night. Cleanshaven, and at noon, he'd never be sure of what welcome he'd get from such a naturally choleric and unpredictable tribe.

*

I forsee a new monastic movement that might replace our present University system. It will be mounted by intellectuals of all kinds, renouncing any part of surrender to the crassness of most politics and all war.

*

When the sun of initiative sets, the subsequent night is frightful.

*

There is a lot to be said for having poets go through their physical life hooded. As masters of time and speaking for a client no less than all mankind, they should not be seen ordering their own groceries, asking for tick or delivering their own ambrosia.

The Muppets

Without wishing to surrender my human passport, I declare a growing regard for The Muppets. They put the absurdities of man's condition under the most disquieting light I've seen for years. Their leader, Kermit the Frog, twitching those agonised folds in his rubbery neck, is a memorial to all the chairmen on this earth who have been tormented by the poverty of talent in his turns and the layers of stone in the heart of his audience.

The two old curmudgeons muttering and glowering from their box, loathing every item in the entertainment set before them, enjoying nothing but the supple fitness of their hatred and the ready wit of their denunciations, are the perfect parody of the vast, churlish, unco-ordinated part of the television audience which takes pleasure in dismissing what is so easily come by. Never have the uncreative had such a field-day. Between one potato crisp and the next they can dismiss with a snort and a twist of the switch the highest expressions of contemporary talent.

Every time I see The Muppets I am convinced that if all the gargoyles on the facade of a cathedral, animated by a grant from the Film Board, could come down and make a show, it would not be unlike Kermit's ineffable circus. It would have the same mixture of devil-worship and insane village gossip.

I must confess that on certain nights of special tension I see Kermit everywhere. I watch people engaged in some discussion of high importance. Suddenly one of them will succumb to a moment of passion or panic. His neck muscles will start moving in the Kermit way and I expect to see the whole monstrous rout of vociferous freaks come stomping in.

In 'Who sank the Lusitania' Winston Churchill was accused of having cunningly abetted the sinking of the great liner. Involving the old patriot in criminal conspiracies has become a ready phobia. Hochhuth in 'Soldiers' branded him as responsible for the killing of Sikorski and the needless raising of Dresden. Stand by for the discovery of a man old enough to have seen Churchill spreading the germs that caused the Black Death.

*

Communities can be very perverse about their civil wars. There is always a tendency to idealise the losers. The more dangerously idiotic and backward the losers the more strenuous the adulation. In numberless works of British fiction, Cromwell is portrayed as a sour psychopath, proceeding from villany to villany through a long curriculum of twitches, spasms, shakes and shrieks. There is even a chocolate advertisement on television in which a Cavalier, after bussing his lady in a coach and munching a bar of the sweetmeat, gets out and flattens one of Cromwell's courtiers. Belittling one of our very few men of political genius is no way to encourage the appearance of another.

*

Whatever a man does after the age of forty should be forgiven because in nine cases out of ten, he is utterly worn out by what has gone on before.

*

Life shares with the onion not merely a gift for producing tears, but a provision of many layers of significance.

On Animals . . .

Wild animals in recent years have had a better public relations deal than the human sector. As we have been progressively revealed as the most raffish, destructive and dirty tribe ever to threaten the globe, animals have had their charm and integrity praised on all hands.

Creatures once denounced as ruthless killers and enemies of men, now get the glad hand treatment once reserved for Valentino and Gable. There must be gorillas so bemused by the warm testimonials written for them by anthropologists, they stand shyly in their jungles wondering what gift to expect, a hand of bananas or a clutch of Nobel Prizes.

Some of the pro-animal propaganda could be misleading. There are probably platoons of people around the earth with torn ears and loose arms waiting for their wounds to heal before suing whatever television company it was that assured them that wolves, baboons, hyenas or what have you are, at heart, an amiable and harmless lot.

Sharks

Sharks are the latest of the animal bogies to be welcomed into the parlour of our affections. In a recent documentary, we had a glimpse into the life of nature's most efficient and dedicated destroyer. Its teeth, hunger and speed in one unimprovable package, it is bad news for the millions who, in an age of paid holidays, congest our beaches and tempt fish.

The shark, in relation to its huge bulk, has the smallest brain in the animal kingdom, so it is not likely to become more moral or less hungry. They eat anything, and post-mortem examinations have shown the stomachs of sharks to be junk-heaps stuffed with such unlikely items as bottles and boots. At first this was thought to be due to the shark's short-sightedness or its habit of closing both eyes when the lust to kill is upon it, which is most of the time.

Scientists now think it is a tactic the shark uses for maintaining stability. A few extra ounces of oil entering the liver can upset the shark's balance and it will take aboard any object that floats by to correct the trouble. This fact will have interest for people who might be indifferent to sharks but who might have wondered what happens to the boots and bottles they fling into the sea.

The scientists also say that when a shark swallows you whole or in part, it is not doing so purely out of malice or hunger. It is simply staking its own territory. The land is ours: we should stay on it. If we stray towards the wet, and the shark gets to know, we are likely to return home reduced. We are also assured that a shark's bite is painless. When the jaws make their big play for me I shall remember this and feel consoled.

Birds

Birds on this earth have every reason for keeping man at a distance. Shot at, snared, plucked, eaten, they have had good cause for hanging on to their powers of flight and keeping their options open. But they have had a pleasant way of misleading men. When Columbus first arrived at the West Indies he mistook a flock of flamingoes for a welcoming committee of Chinamen. Dylan Thomas feeding his surrealist vein on his adopted estuary, stared at the herons outside his front door, and saw something solemn and oracular in their bearing and movement. He felt West Wales to be filling up with some new kind of priestly convention.

Wolves

There must be a streak of real perversity in wolves for they certainly elect to do it the hard way. The intervals of ease in their lives are brief and tormentingly nervous. No species works harder or travels further on horrible terrain to get its simple fare, caribou slain on the hoof. When the pack tracks down and kills its prey the pack leader and his mate get the first choice of the richest meat. This is to ensure that they will have that bit of extra strength to guide the pack on to its next target and the cunning to get them out of trouble, and trouble in these dark, unfriendly areas has its hand permanently on the knocker. The wolf, though, unless you happen to be sitting in a failing sleigh with the wolf's battle-wail getting louder in your ears, is an impressive animal. It looks after its children, keeps its house clean and doesn't worry too much about the cost of living.

The Beaver
This animal has a gift of industry that would have won him his own chapel in the high noon of the Puritan work ethic.

He has something against running water and fells trees and dams streams to make tranquil lakes and ravishing new ecologies. Throw the beaver a few extra nuts and he'd have that projected levee thrown across the Bristol Channel in less time than it takes to say hydraulic power. He is a civil engineer of genius who does not give a damn about differentials. There must be powerful factions in the animal world which think that the beaver overdoes it.

Otters
Of all creatures currently nursing a grouch about the present validity and future prospects of earthly existence, otters must be among those with the best grounds for complaint. With an agility and grace of movement that make even the most athletic of men seem crass and leaden, the otter has been driven into a few shrinking corners of our countryside.

Men have been after it with cudgels and hounds ever since brutality was first organised into a catalogue of hobbies. Now drainage schemes and pollution are limiting ancient sources of food. Without marshes, titbits like frogs are hard to come by.

Otters must be wandering through a maze of new hungers. A web of dementing frustrations must be falling over whole fringes of the animal world. One small consoling thought is that it is almost as hard for a human to get hold of a fish as it is for an otter. We must find ways of getting this across to the otter. I wouldn't want it to imagine that we are wolfing fish by the ton while its own world empties of joy, sense and protein.

Elephants

Speaking from inside a thin, penetrable human skin and a frail, vulnerable human mind, it is refreshing to think about elephants. They are solid upon the earth, impenitently antique in form and not likely to be deceived or put upon.

We saw a good slice of their lives in David Attenborough's film 'Elephant Kingdom'. An Englishman, Bill Woods, who has worked in the teak forests of Thailand and used the labour of elephants all his life, provided a fine, dry commentary. These expatriates who have accepted the life of the East and cease to pine for Europe, make fascinating witnesses, disenchanted as an empty gin bottle but endlessly acute.

'In the old days,' he said, 'we would write to a friend in another forest. We always ended the letter 'Hope you are well', ' but they never were. 'In the rains we had malaria once a month.' He went on, 'Elephants are the nicest and brightest of the animals. Of course they kill from time to time. I have seen them kneel on a man and sometimes they pick him up and break him on their tusks.'

It surprised me to see elephants as an organised work force. I had imagined the trunk to be a kind of overgrown frontal brain lobe that would steer them clear of servitude. But there they were, wearing chains and hauling teak.

There is a religious aura around their capture and training. When a man is away from home on an elephant hunt, the wife must eschew finery and extra-marital affairs or the man might suffer, for the elephant's dignity will have been debased by such folly. That is the best suggestion television has given us to date for cutting down on our bills for millinery and divorce.

I watched the film so closely that if I am set down among elephants I think I'll be able to cope. One steers them with constant pressure of the feet behind their ears. When they transfer water from trunk to mouth the spillage is enormous. If ever you tried teaching an elephant table manners you'd wind up with a dirty table.

Even with their bulk they still have less pulling power than horses. I'm sure that if they were more stupid they could pull their present load with a couple of horses sitting on top of it. But they don't let on. That shows how smart they are. They qualify for the vote and would, given a roomier voting booth, use it interestingly. But like the rest of the animal kingdom, save those hooked on tinned dog food and cat food, they are waiting for man to go away.

Turtles

For anyone with a corner to spare in his pity, or prayer for creatures gravely at odds with the free-wheeling cycle of birth, struggle, loss and reparation, I recommend the baby turtle to his earnest attention. The turtles, in terms of speed and beauty, live minimally. Nature has gone to extreme lengths to make half-wits out of turtles. Their evolution came to a stop at the outset of an Ice Age and after a few aeons of shivering thought decided to call it a day. They are wide open to outrage. If turtles could write, libraries would be sadder places.

They stand to get their quittance from as ripe a team of tearing miscreants as you are likely to find outside a major gaol. There are vultures which uncover the pits of eggs in the sand, and only those eggs survive that fall below the vulture's level of satiety, and it is rarely sated. You've got to hand it to vultures. If you don't they'll take it anyway.

If you hear a strange noise in the night it is vultures commenting on man's many complaints about his shortages. 'What's with you kid? We find it easy enough.'

Once the baby turtles are out of the egg, nature becomes all eye and tooth and goes in with the punch. After the vultures comes a species of racoon called the cotamundi. Then the iguana which waddles like a palais-de-danse masher on a good Saturday night. If these predators happen to be resting there is the ghost-crab which is pale, fast, multi-eyed and remorseless. Above them is the frigate bird, a slick and voracious diner, which seems to be tasting the victim with its wings before moving in with the beak.

But the last probability of doom facing the infant turtle as it scurries towards the safety of the sea on those pitifully inept flappers is that its mother, returning to lay a fresh clutch of eggs, will crush it to death as it lumbers up to make its deposit. If it survives all this it might find its way to the soup in a Lord Mayor's banquet and take its leave of earthly traffic with at least a little dignity.

If the United Nations have a genuine care for harassed communities then I suggest that they create a vast college to instruct turtles in the fine human arts of deviousness and fierce self-defence.

The Condor
The vulture has always been a symbol of unpleasantness. Its strength and length of wing, the hint of total callousness in its great beak, the caricatured pantaloons around its legs have always made it a ready image for the less attractive type of plutocrat who swoops around human society treating the living with the kind of savage discourtesy the vulture reserves for the dead. With a proper complement of top hats and cigars, the vulture would have been ennobled in most lands.

Indeed as the total landscape of human behaviour

comes into view, the vulture becomes almost amiable. And vultures become rarer. We are capable of deep affection for creatures that have given a virtual pledge to perish shortly.

The South American vulture, the condor, sweeps up and down the Andes, terrifying other birds and helping earth's sanitation, disposer of extinguished lives, a gliding grave. In the early days of aviation among the great peaks of Chile and Peru, the condor could be a nightmare to pilots. After mortal confrontations in the high passes, the mix-up was so total that many passengers finished the journey by condor and demanded a rebate when they hopped off the condor's back at Mexico City. In some Mexico villages condors are lashed to the back of a bull. The bull symbolises the Spanish conqueror. If the condor survives and lives to fly back into the mountains, the Indian dreams that he might one day restore the glories of his ancient Maya and Inca civilisations. The condor, as I said, grows rarer. So, I am sure, do dreams of resurrection.

Human stupidity can in part be explained by the amount of genius that is dispersed through species that go their own immortal and indifferent way in the air, under the earth and beneath the sea. Many talents denied to the human skull abound in living things whose existence we snuff out with every step we take.

*

If bees knew how good they looked in colour they would work through an agent. Among the human pollinators are emerging pop-groups to whom I would deny fertility in any shape or form.

*

Students of animal behaviour have for decades been experimenting with rats. They have come up with a truth deduced by the first men in the first caves. If rats are congested in a rigidly limited environment, the rats grow less charming. Cordiality among people who lived in each other's pockets is so precariously based it is always looking for a chance to vanish.

Voids of Unfulfilment

Look with care at most lives and you will see collapsed areas, cratered places where the topsoil never achieved the depth of richness to allow some favoured dream to sprout and grow. We are registered, taxed, used, but our real identity is rarely known. We cry out in the dark our true name, nature, desire, but no one replies, no one cares.

In the spaces of the soul we carry voids of unfulfilment. And in each void we light a candle of veneration before some chosen hero, some mythical figure who spoke, moved, fought, made love or money as we would wish to have done. The world's heroes are laid like poultices on the world's inadequacies. The sexually deprived, the bald and people who can't tell their left foot from the other, will dream of being another George Best. The gauche and timid who marry shabbily after ten years of courtship and who will never have handled a weapon more offensive than a bar-room dart, will salute James Bond and call him brother. In their private thoughts they will pluck nubile berries from every passing bush, shoot Slavs and all who mock at Public School standards and settle for chastity and rough snacks.

Hereward the Wake will be the hero of those who would prefer to hide among reeds in an uncharted marsh rather than face conquerors who trample the land. The vast majority, more modest and less dramatic in their fantasies, will fix their fancy on that genial, undefeatable moron, Yogi Bear. Whenever I am in a crowded place I see so many people looking like Yogi I keep glancing around for those park wardens to come and keep us all in order.

Mastermind

That very superior quiz, 'Mastermind', returns each year to dazzle us. So many entertainments of this sort dip down into a wanton imbecility to cater for the potent hill-billy element in the viewing population that "Mastermind" strikes a note of outright starkness. The set helps that impression along. The contestants advance to the ordeal along what looks like a gang-plank. The chair has a chilling plainness that calls to mind if not something as august as the Day of Judgment, at least something as grimly final as the old take-off night at Sing-Sing.

I am struck by the disparity in the areas of knowledge offered by the competitors. Some will elect to do academic battle in a vast meadow of known fact like the Roman Empire in Britain or British Parliamentary history since 1870, German literature since Goethe, things that would take half a lifetime to arrange tidily in the mind for prompt finding and presenting at the sight of Mr. Magnus Magnusson. Another will choose to occupy a cosy little corner like the novels of Jane Austen, of which an average alert reader will master all the details in six months.

Yet, for most of us, each contestant will achieve his own little miracle of knowledge and memory and, not least, pure, cold-blooded valour in the face of an unnerving trial.

If the Popes had had to win their name for infallibility by means as gruelling as these, things would have been a lot quieter at Rome. The great Pontiffs could, at least, wrestle for their authority on thrones, alone, and in the dark if the fancy took them, not under a spotlight, on that awful chair, with multitudes waiting to see them go flat on their faces.

But we are spared the histrionics of some quiz victims. The aspiring master-minds accept the occasional blow of ignorance as calmly as Socrates took his hemlock.

They do not roll their eyes or slap their brows as if trying to strike a hint of dawn and waking into snoring brains. They do not utter that infuriating whimper, 'It's on the tip of my tongue,' which one hears so often in less exacting jousts one has the vision of tongues the size of aircraft carriers. 'Pass' they say, and half smile, as if their minds were fractious children guilty of a tiny, pardonable lapse.

I watched the 'Eurovision Song Contest' with idle ears, mobile eyes and emerged with my misanthropy intact.

*

'The Lone Ranger' doubled the debility of the average television plot by having the Ranger wear a mask at all times. His identity was known only to his horse who never talked. He also had a constant companion, an Apache brave called Tonto, whose English was too poor for coherent revelations. If the sponsors only knew the Lone Ranger's thoughts about his Red Indian friend, Tonto, they would cancel the programme, pronto.

*

The Royal Variety Command Performance which made last Sunday the longest Sabbath since the Lord's first Day of Rest, must be republicanism's most powerful secret weapon.

Raining Bankers

The American slump of 1929 was one of the world's most interesting convulsions before the ripened nightmare finally burst ten years later. It differed from all previous disasters of an economic kind. Never had a community toppled from such a height of affluence and optimism. Never had pride and greed been so well organised or widely diffused.

From the millionaire's heir to the modest artisan every American had his lassoo out to bring the Golden Calf to its knees for hauling off to his barbecue pit. The formal equality of the ballot box was to be matched by an equal bulge in the pocket book. The gloomy doctrines of Marx and the International Workers of the World were to be buried with no requiem longer than a short horse laugh.

Then along every Main Street in America it started raining bankers. Deflated partners, if they had joint accounts, leaped through windows hand in hand. Al Capone made the front pages buying apples from emaciated panhandlers on the principle that an apple a day keeps the Vice Squad away.

The chicken that Herbert Hoover promised to put in every pot got up and bit him and the pot went into pawn. The Depression also differed from all others in having found an extra dimension of self-consciousness. Cinema and radio pickled the sights and sounds of the great absurdity. Anguish, to the everlasting discomfiture of the replete, would never again be silent and invisible.

Electronic Phantoms

People, to make their houses look more personal and lived in, will stuff their rooms with the most unlikely things. Men and women who have, for decades, worn their past like a tight skin, will part with nothing that reminds them of warmer, lovelier times. A mountain of trivialities piles up around them, infinitely precious to them, symptoms of a deepening madness to the passing observer. The stuffing is all, our ultimate defence against the advancing cold.

The finest stuffing, for a mind painfully aware of empty, threatening places, is the serial story. Radio and television have provided serials of a length and credibility that make them a layman's liturgy of belief in the principle of vital continuity. These creatures of fiction become in odd ways guarantees of our own immortality. They stand on the outer walls of our consciousness. We await their daily or weekly return and their predictable prattle is as consoling as the watchman's 'All's well', assuring us that some part of the citadel still stands.

There's not a jot of harm in this. Most of our passions are spent on ghosts. And the electronic phantoms are at our command. We let them in or keep them out. They are never as tyrannical as the shadows of yearning and remorse that sit on their mushroom throne in the centre of most minds. Fiction is altogether a better bet than fact.

I once knew a man whose life had been shattered by misfortune that came roaring from every corner of the sky. He preserved his sanity, or lost it, by going to see the film of 'The Desert Song' wherever it was shown. Twice he was whipped into hospital with sand-fever and ingrowing mirages. But he recovered his health. His spirit rose again and he saved up enough to go on a package tour to Morocco where he broke his arm falling off a camel. Even as he fell, he told the camel it was worth it.

But let us not despise the mills of fictional nonsense. The makers of your endless serials wear their brains to shreds as diligently as your statesmen or astral physicists. And balderdash, dished out more imperially then ever before, simply does what the fairy tale has immemorially done: it tries to blunt the edge of life's high gift of instilling terror and boredom.

The only difference is that the cigar which does duty as Sir Lew Grade's wand turns to ashes more quickly than the usual sort. We must not expect too much from a medium that gives too much. To enter fully into the kingdom of the poet, we are told, we must suspend disbelief. In coming to terms with the lower levels of television story telling it is not enough merely to suspend disbelief. You should shoot it out of hand before switching on.

I have two examples of dedicated nonsense in mind. They hold millions in thrall and there is no lunatic improbability they will not welcome in and make thoroughly at home.

The first is a thing called a 'Voyage to the Bottom of the Sea' which is another name for the bottom of the barrel. This concerns a submarine. The vessel is part of America's first line of defence. You might think that just being in a submarine is bad enough. But this thing runs into a belt of nightmare situations that must have packed a whole wing of some Californian asylum with exhausted scriptwriters.

It confirms one's suspicion that America has done as much for paranoia as for the popular song. In one episode a cabbage, innocently smuggled aboard, begins endlessly to swell, filling the ship with trouble and Vitamin C. In another the sub activates the ghost of Edward Teach, the pirate Blackbeard, who anticipated the cigarette lighter by threading his huge beard with gunpowder and igniting it whenever he wished to confuse an enemy.

One instalment showed us creatures made of stone slabs. We assume that they were once human but were petrified by some grim cosmic surprise a few aeons back. Even under water they are still socially organised, sitting on the ocean's bed like a municipal rockery. I would name them the least charming entities ever devised even in the whacky realm of reckless fiction. I wish the 'Seaview' a long cruise. It makes the grotesque realities of living seem utterly palatable.

A suitable pendant to 'Voyage' is 'Dr. Who'. This series pounds interminably at the back door of the imagination. At the hub of the affair is some impresario of mischief called the Master. In one episode he invoked tailed devils to take over a village church and filled the vacuum left by the departing tithe. In another the Master's flock were creatures whose top-half was frog and whose bottom half was roughly trousered.

In a recent fling the Master said: 'Get stubs and cotton and disinfect the atmosphere around this planet.' I was wondering what these implements might be and how they would be used to do this cleaning job on the air when two myrmidons came in. They were Stubbs and Cotton. If you watch long and keenly enough you will always learn something. One of the writers of 'Dr. Who' and creator of the Daleks, Terry Nation, spent his early years around Pendoylan, in the Vale of Glamorgan. I wonder what he saw in the quiet lanes of those placid acres that the rest of us have missed. With the progressive withdrawal of buses I hope one day to board the last Dalek to Pontyclun.

The Duke of Wellington fought Napoleon to a standstill at Waterloo and almost did as much for adult suffrage at Westminster. He would no more have trusted a working man with the vote than he would have presented Jack the Ripper with a canteen of cutlery.

*

History is largely a matter of where you happen to be standing or sitting at the time. Memory is often even more defective than the eyesight which registered the first impression. The more exciting or alarming the event, the less reliable the record is likely to be.

*

I suppose that most people crossed the time frontier of nineteen hundred cheering, confident that the new techniques of power and swelling resources of wealth would lift mankind clear of the old perils and indignities. We are still picking the shrapnel of that shattered pipe-dream out of our scalp.

*

Theology has taken wing since my time among the young. Priorities change like the weather. A day will come when the old religious urge to protect our boys and girls from the experience of sin, will be replaced by an equally passionate demand that they be introduced to the experience of paid work and simple courtesy.

Reflections on Extravagance

I must say that when the enterprise 'War and Peace' was launched I shied away from it a little. The advance publicity was so loud I covered my ears and checked on possible bolt-holes for the next five months.

The book itself is such an ikon one's nerves stiffen a bit at the mention of it. Millions have presented their reading of it as a medal of literacy. Kingsley Martin of the New Statesman was blown off the bathroom seat by a German bomb while reading it. He was blown from the same place by another bomb a little later while reading Jane Austen, so the story is in no way levelled critically against Tolstoy.

Then there was the colossal expense and trouble involved in making the serial. I think it foolish of television with its surgical-belt budgets and vast output to ape Hollywood and Elstree at their florid and wasteful best.

I read, glumly unimpressed, the amounts of money to be spent on ballrooms, banquets, fox-hunts, battles. When these things have been done adequately for the cinema, television should leave them alone. If a television executive should see a young producer smouldering with a wish to break away from one-shot kitchen drama and do a Cecil B. de Mille with half the world as extras, he should be given a condition powder and told to take another look at kitchens.

For, clearly, to make an epic on a shoe-string means somebody is going to be strangled. The resources will be strained to yield that last droplet of effect. If you hire eight wagons every wheel must be shown. If you engage a thousand soldiers every leg must come into view, every detail of their ill-fitting costumes must be given star-billing. The viewer will grow so fed up with marionettes marching through smoke, shedding simulated blood from artfully manufactured scars, he will long for a telescoping of the journey to see Moscow burned and poor neurotic, bitched up Andrei and Pierre at some kind of peace.

And one has thoughts of those portions of the Yugoslav army that are constantly advancing or retreating in these spectacles. It is just as well that Tito implanted a vigorous guerilla tradition in his land, for if Yugoslavia is ever invaded at least four large budget movies and television blockbusters will have to be suspended to get anybody into the front line.

In a play of this kind the lavish set-pieces have an impressive but clogging quality. Television is a quick, gossipy medium. The secret of the cinema as a myth maker was the huge screen, the odorous darkness and the fact that one was surrounded by a mob of naive, impressionable people gasping with astonishment that such marvels were being unfurled. Television spectacle, like television snacks, should err on the small side.

In the ballroom sequence in 'War and Peace', every dress and chandelier are seen until the watching eye begins to rustle and glimmer. It is rather like a session of competitive dancing performed under heavy sedation. When aristocratic guests sit down to dine every bit of expensive china is faithfully recorded. One's senses are poured out with the soup. Distinguished jaws are observed champing over every mouthful of Tsarist nosh and one is driven to the wine cupboard to keep the juices going until such time as the plot decides to move again. And fictional battles, surely, in a century when the truth itself about the awful, bloody business has been ground into the retina, should be considered a mere bewilderment and bore, except perhaps for children, and even they'd have reservations.

But the achievement was mighty. The opening and closing music, the old imperial hymn, caught the mind as poignantly as the sight of woodsmoke on the steppes touched the mind of Turgenev. Their anthem was one of the few good things about the Tsars.

There are areas in the shell of social sanity that are more than usually brittle. Depress them and whole societies will march into rounds of lunatic excess at the drop of a slogan.

*

Alter society as you will, bewilderment at the wounding of the heart remains man's basic culture.

*

Humanity backed a loser when it split into men and women.

GWYN THOMAS

Shadow of a Gunman

Write something for the theatre which chills the blood, darkens the heart yet manages to exalt and exhilarate the mind and you have a play which will add an inch or two to life. Such a work is 'Shadow of a Gunman', by Sean O'Casey. Ireland is one of the shadier miracles of the present age. Historians, mild men with a strong taste for murder at second-hand and who feed with relish on social perversity, will record the Irish Question as one of the most damnable anomalies ever to persist in the context of so wily and imaginative a political entity as the British Isles.

The grappling relationship of England with Ireland has involved some permanent brain damage. The passage of the Celtic Sea has prompted a rhythmic delirium of the kind that might result from a combined flood of Irish and Scottish whiskies.

Sean O'Casey was in a masterly position to see the shambles whole and clear. He was brought up as an Irish Protestant and also fought in the Easter Rebellion of 1916. He had a foot on each of the two great myths: the Ascendancy and the dream of Ireland Redeemed.

He was also gripingly poor and a genius, a crippling conjunction. I would say that what was left over from his hatred of Ireland he transferred willingly to humanity as a whole. Never has a gaiety of words moved on a vehicle of such acrid sadness and contempt. 'Poet and poltroon' are the last damning words of 'Shadow of a Gunman'.

The poetry O'Casey expressed is the most brilliant humour in this century. And into the flesh of the poltroon O'Casey drove his pen like a dagger. His plays are loud with men whose courage and character have gone up on smoky rhetoric and self-delusion long since.

The vicious, preservative illusions, our version of a day-to-day, do-it-yourself death are back on parade. In the terrorist context, bombs and the horror they bring on, are the simplest element.

The explosive ruptures in the minds of those who find no efficient or tolerable part in the absurdity are much more deadly. To my mind, Donal Davoren, the young poet lost and sick in the trap of violence, and Minnie Powell, the spirited Republican lass, homing in on to her appointed bullet, as lovers nailed to death on the stupid irony of their time, are a thousand times more moving than Romeo and Juliet.

Newton should have stayed in the orchard a little longer and deduced a law about the gravitational pull that death and ruin exercise on the human will.

*

To the average contemporary mind, overprivilege and excessive wealth have begun to take on a slightly monstrous air. The democratic spirit wants luck more thinly and evenly spread.

*

I wish there were a potter and a wheel to mould in perfection the survival policies of modern man.

Piltdown Jokers?

According to the researchers described in 'The Ape That Stood Up', a documentary presented by the daughter of the eminent Dr. Leakey, who made discoveries in a Kenyon gorge that pointed to man being a much more mature article than we had imagined, 30,000 years is just a sigh, a week-end, a day off. I had always sensed that this might be so, but I kept mum about it, not wishing to upset anyone.

Skulls of a plainly human type have now been found in East Africa that might be no younger than three million years. They have brain-pans of human capacity that might have housed an intelligence comparable with the one that today fills in the pools coupons and drives fast in fog. Bones of arms and legs found on the same site prove these pioneers to have had joint structures as complex and competently prehensile as ours.

These relics were found beneath a layer of volcanic ash which geologists, always eager to give volcanic ash a better opinion of itself, date as being at least two and a half million years old.

This will confirm the age of the skulls for everyone except those who, like myself in certain twilit moods of aching disbelief, hold that the earth is infested not only with bones but with Piltdown jokers who specialise in finding very old layers of volcanic ash and propping them up with a few up-to-date skulls to fool earnest searchers like Dr. Leakey and the vast army of people who welcome each new television documentary in a spirit of credulous submission.

Disappearing World

Programmes like 'Disappearing World' deal with pockets of humanity that are likely very soon to be snipped away from the human community by hunger, sterility and the greed of vigorous men intent on driving roads through the wilderness and despoiling forests.

Ongka is a minor chieftain and a major clown. The tribe he bosses is primitive and contentedly idle. Missionaries and the Australian Government which protects them have persuaded them that their old habit of eating people is discourteous. So they cultivate more sweet potatoes and develop the tensions that set in when a deep, traditional pleasure has been withdrawn.

Ongka gave us a summary of how the Modern State came into being, as a blend of fear, concern and candid racketeering. Ongka has the job of collecting a large gift to the Government, large enough to put the authorities into an everlasting state of benevolence. The gift will be of pigs, the Papuan's chief domestic animal.

Ongka is a pig-obsessed man. He cajoles and threatens his parishioners to get their quota of swine together for the big day of giving, when Ongka will don a complete suit of ceremonial feathers to impress any white brothers who might drop in to collect the tribute. It is uphill work. Ongka made a speech to a group of villagers. 'This gift will deliver us from shame and anxiety. But you are behind with your pig target. You swill beer and fool about with women. I am angry with you.'

As soon as Ongka's back is turned the villagers turn over, reach for a pint and call for a cuddle. Ongka wears a poked cap that looks as if it might have been discarded by an itinerant brass-bandsman. His praetorial technique is formidable: a mixture of warble, gargle and yodel underlined by glottal stops that shake the forest, and sustained bellows that remind one of Jerry Colonna, that moustached foghorn who once worked with Bob Hope.

In Ongka's society there are simplicities now denied to the Western World. He was asked what would happen if their parliamentary member did not return the kindness expressed in the gift of pigs. 'We take him behind a bush and slit his throat.' And then the owner of the bush comes comes along and seconds the amendment. I am glad that Ongka is where he is, out on his doomed periphery. With his skills, that cap and all the pork, he would, planted among us, become a very corrupt politician indeed.

⳩⳩⳩

I have never warmed to quiz programmes since, at the age of nine, I was made one of a panel in the rigorous Bible quiz in a local vestry. The organiser was a bearded, severe man, not God but the next best thing, the man who looked after the colliery dynamite. His first question to me was: 'Give me the names of the only three men in the New Testament whose names begin with F'. Desperate, I tried him with Frank as a starter. I was thrown off the platform, given a Bible with letters that lit up and excused panel duty for the rest of my days.

*

I had a look at the old film 'Wilson' and confirmed my belief that the League of Nations failed because it knew this film was going to be made about it.

The Bully and the Box

From the earliest flicker of the silent cinema, moving pictures have planted minefields in the human imagination. Our impulse to imitate took on a whole new dimension when we started to stare at screens that jumped with animated projections.

There is a man, still hale, in the uplands of Mid-Glamorgan, who in his childhood fell into a phobia of affection for the comedians of the silent cinema. He could do them all. Chaplin, Keaton, Turpin, Harry Langdon, all, of course, without a single verbal clue to what he was about.

His turn worked a treat with fellow buffs. But he often took part in talent contests organised by the chapels. The adjudicators at these events were often men who had never set foot inside a cinema. One of these judges, brought to a peak of nervous illness by a long series of failures and calamities, was presiding over a Go-As-You-Please in which this boy was taking part with his lightning panorama of Hollywood comedy's golden age.

The judge tried to take it all in. He gave up the ghost convinced that his mind had reached the final bend of the road. He shot out of the vestry as if the whole league of spectral hounds were after him, his cracked laughter bounced back and forth by the wondering hillsides.

Radio added to the echo-shop. A lad of my acquaintance became addicted to a long-running series called 'The Man From Mars'. The Martian whose name was Olion, was played by an actor with a deep, commanding voice. My friend's loyalty to this person grew stronger. He would buttonhole sages in the Workmen's Library and put searching questions to them about Mars, suggesting now and then that the distant star would one day oust Barry and Porthcawl as the object of our outings.

He would go into shops and tell the shopkeeper with his stiff, alien tones he had picked up from the radio-actor,

'Me, Olion, Man from Mars'. The shopkeeper, after ten years of slump, thought that things were tough enough already without having messages of this sort passed over the counter. They complained and my friend was told to stop it and stay earthly. My friend heeded the warning and switched off Olion. But even now when puzzled by some new aspect of strangeness, his voice will drop to a point below his waistcoat and his eyes will fill with interplanetary gleams. No real harm done.

But with television the echoes grew louder and more sinister. During the early years of post-war television I had no set of my own, finding in the cinema all the pictorial sublimation I needed.

But the majority of the boys I taught had sets, and I had the nightmarish experience of seeing the boys sitting in front of me bewitched by the new medium, lapsing into imitative worlds of fantasy to which I held no key.

There was one lad so sensitive to what was coming out of Lime Grove and the other television centres, he could have been submitted as a comprehensive jar to any exposition of psychoneurotic disturbances. In the days of innocence he would use jerky limbs and falsetto squeaks to give his classmates the flavour of Muffin the Mule and Bill and Ben the flowerpot-men. During these simulations, he would put on an expression of such baleful inanity, I have never been able to see a donkey or a flower since without looking over both shoulders.

As the medium became more complex, he broadened his range. Whenever the teacher's back was turned he would be summarising the previous evening's output for those boys still without a set. During the Quatermass Experiment period he slowed down the academic progress of most of his classmates by recreating for them the full horror of the spongy octopal mass proliferating in the drains of Holborn. He was also good at establishing a British staging-post for an American Western series called 'Rawhide'.

His speciality there was to reproduce every twitch and grimace of an actor called Paul Binegar, who played a cantankerous wagon-trail cook always full of whining invective about the monotony of beans, the size of the West, the smell of beeves. I once saw the whole of this performance through the classroom window and it had the same effect on me as those impressions of Ben Turpin and Lloyd Hamilton had on that morose, diaconal judge who briefly let go his marbles a generation ago.

But in all my teaching years I recall only one boy whose departure from the normal had anything to do with television. The lad's father was a merchant seaman. The home background was bad. Both parents were shiftless. The house was badly furnished and when the father brought home a portable set from abroad, it struck the only note of twentieth century elegance beneath that particular roof.

The boy became besotted by it. He stared at the tiny screen with such hungry intensity he created the effect of Pasteur confronting a new miracle of healing. His new rapture made some of the masters in the school mark the boy down as prime Sixth Form material, a verdict which would have surprised the boy. The only thing in his head were the synopses of every shown episode of 'William Tell', 'Robin Hood' and 'The Buccaneers'.

He showed his father a fresh respect for having brought this portent into their kitchen. The father took to boasting about the set in the pub. He was overheard by a local burglar, a maliciously envious as well as larcenous man. He stole the set. The boy suffered a severe mental shock. The squalor of his home, the inadequacy of his parents, were revealed in a crudely new light.

His temper worsened. He took to beating up his friends who still had access to the visual dope. He proceeded naturally from this discourtesy to theft. He injured himself while trying to get one of the very early colour sets through a small window, and was sent for remedial treatment by a court that took a simple view of these things.

Television as the supposed inspirer of wrong-doing has become a convenient whipping-boy. Here we are living in a society where all the raw materials of good conduct are being whittled away, and for every new lurch from the old norms of decency we blame the mechanical trifler in the corner, which is of little more significance than yesterday's gossip over the back wall. It is as grotesquely wrong an analysis as anything in the ju-ju cults which blamed lightning and flood on mistakes made in the utterance of prayer.

Within the last generation forms of conduct that were once gigantic bastions against hooliganism have fallen. Mothers of my mother's generation accepted that their lives would begin and end with the making, the training, the feeding and the clothing of any number of children.

My mother had twelve children, did her valiant best for all of them and died in her early forties. Whether her reflective ghost would regard that experience as a monstrous wasteful trick or as a natural fate she would accept again is a question that continues to bother my mind. Of one thing only am I sure. She would have liked television, whenever she was able to see or hear the thing through the mob of cormorants that thronged our tiny kitchen.

Her world rested on a compost of willing sacrifice. Sacrifice has become a word one spits on. We have run out of suckers. Bitter wisdom filtering like a dirty rain through the broken roofs of our society has become the tide of the day. Much of it has come from television. Never has social conduct and social power ever been so extensively and disrespectfully analysed. People who in 1877 would have walked over twenty miles of moorland to listen to Mr. Gladstone outlining his portrait of the New Jerusalem, now yawn or chuckle in bored incredulity as they listen to the political telecast that tells them that Britain's troubles are now on the mend.

We have allowed patterns of rehousing that have written new charters of freedom for misery and madness. We have thrown away many of the devices that once kept fools in awe and their implulses in tidy subjugation. Once we had teachers who held the golden belief that they were men to revere or at least that they were creatures of greater worth and substance than their pupils.

Such an attitude today would be derided as dangerously pompous. The teacher who thinks an unremitting matey-ness and familiarity are the keys to his pupils' hearts will soon find himself in schools where Tarzan swings in for his annual trip of inspection.

The teacher who kicks away his pedestal steps on to a gallows. Future grants in aid to intending teachers should include a monster bonus for a starch of self-pride, self-confidence, that will shine in the night and keep any prospective louts humble and cautious.

The Middle Ages, the epoch of modesty and submission on the part of the ordinary folk, ended with the coming of the television commercial. These brilliant little messages, potent as the prayer-systems that created the cathedrals, have created new landscapes of desire in the contemporary mind. We deluge the imagination with concepts of idyllic ease on sunlit beaches and lush meadows, with an endless feast of chocolate and expensive booze thrown in and still expect men and women to file, with raptures of loyalty, into pits and factories.

That, and not the occasional punch-up between cops and robbers, is the great new element that television has brought into today's morality. There were once moods in our society that were favourable to kindliness. They no longer operate on the minds of the sullen little cynics who wait in the shadows to perform their nightly rites of malevolence and mischief.

Some will say there are too many of us watching too much television. This is a silly irrelevance. There are too many of us, full stop. We have exhausted the genius of mercantile and industrial society. Millions feel trapped and resentful. Without the opiate distraction of television the havoc wrought by the vandal would have been far greater.

On the positive side, for every one who will be tempted to molest their neighbours there will be tens of thousands moved to a new gentleness by television's devotion to the various aspects of conservation.

I once heard a man confess to me that he had spent a day contemplating violence against a neighbour. That evening he saw a film about mutual aid among dolphins. The sedulous compassion of the great fish changed his view of life. He gave his neighbour a loaf in the middle of a baker's strike.

Laughter has its own sacred priestly function to perform. It cools the wrath of the fanatic. It leavens the stupidity of the pompous dolt.

*

One of man's commonest hobbies is to predict that we are going to land in the soup.

*

With coffee at its present price, who will say that Dracula's line of beverages was altogether wrong?

Poultices of Stone

It is impressive that creatures as distraught and brittle as men should have left behind so many monuments of calm and lasting dignity. On the wounds of our eternal plotting and bickering we have laid some marvellous poultices of stone. Our great buildings are a form of apology we make for the insults we have levelled with such diligence at ourselves and the earth. In these ancient buildings man has pooled all the grace and harmony he witholds from his day-to-day intercourse. With testimonials like these our species could get any job it applied for.

The great cathedrals, monasteries and early universities were built as talismans against the evils of plague and violence which few men could analyse or withstand. Men raised cathedrals to express an exultant hope. They went into monasteries and colleges to qualify the hope with second thoughts about the whole thing.

In the master-works of the post-mediaeval period, the odour of divinity wanes and the smell of the human individual is pungent in the land.

Blenheim Palace and Castle Howard are the perfect memorials of a period when a powerful few had the confidence and strength to tell the responsive mass to shut up and get on with it.

I liked the story of John Churchill, first Duke of Marl-borough, tormented by the problem of draughts in huge buildings. He gave his carpenters stern instructions on the sort of joinery he expected on his doors and windows. On his first night in the completed palace he had all the candles lit in all the corridors. He inspected each candle. Not a flame wavered. That might have been a comment either on the state of the building or the state of the Duke. If you were a candle-flame and you were being examined by a man given almost divine status for downing the French, you would wriggle at your peril.

Autumn, on television, is the season of the hyena, the animal that keeps on laughing without any particular reason and against all the predatory odds. As the summer limps back out of sight, wits shorten with the hours of sunlight. The various channels of entertainment darken with gross and desperate infusions of the comic spirit. All those not wishing to be amused to death will do well to wear protective pads around the funny bone. For nothing is surer than that as the troubles of the world at large and of this nation in particular thicken and multiply, so will the efforts of the television magnates to open up every avenue of giggling escape.

The aim will be to keep us all in a state of unfeeling trance, and every trick, short of strapping ether-tanks to the side of sets, will be deployed.

Even in the graveyards there must be departed stand-up comedians who get twice-nightly to their feet to plague the quieter residents with a wish to crack a fresh gag over death's old head. Hamlet did not stumble across Yorick's skull. Yorick came to him, with a couple of new ones.

A man may be talking the most sublime sense imaginable, but one listens to it less attentively if he suspends the flow from time to time to spread a good inch of cream cheese on to a cracker. I like profundity and I like cheese, but rigidly separate.

*

Hunger does not sharpen wits, it destroys them. A vast section of humanity is being cretinised for lack of a timely crust.

*

We distribute what little we have with an unfairness that touches lunacy at many points. The U.S.A. with only six per cent of the world's population uses thirty per cent of the world's energy supplies. I took that fact aboard on an evening when my sympathy with mankind had waxed over a supper of stuffed onions. I slept badly.

The Christmas View

I hear complaints that television is making too private and muffled a thing of Christmas. The roaring jollity of yester-year is dead. People sit besotted by the lighted, lavish miracle in the parlour corner, lapped in warm waves of alien corn, oblivious of the old order of hospitality. I find lovers of the conventional feast speaking bitterly of latter-day Scrooges, televictims, who draw blinds and bolt doors against the furtive waifs who are currently depressing the choral urge to its official nadir, who knock, wail briefly and depart, leaving mounds of mutilated carols in their wake.

I do not share these protests. My own early Christmases were excessively public. I was one of a Band of Hope troupe that staged an annual Yuletide spectacular. I was one of twelve lads dressed up as reindeer, with imitation antlers that left at least seven of us unstable in later life.

The musical director was a man who had contracted delusions of grandeur instead of the customary rickets and ringworm, and he kept making the sleigh bigger every year. He was eager to lift South Wales out of what he considered its trough of hymnal gloom and subversive wrath.

The regular Santa was a huge baritone who pressed his full weight on the vehicle, making it impossible for the twelve human stags to budge it an inch. He was the only brake who could sit tight and sing flat for a whole evening. He was a bit of a sadist. He was supposed to flick our antlers with his whip but malevolence was his Christmas treat. He was so much like Captain Bligh his sleigh was probably full of breadfruit, and his thong connected as often as not with our shoulders. At the final curtain we lay bitter, bruised and bleeding in the traces.

We did little better with carols. We sang outside three houses only and from each we were driven by the barking of dogs. Two of the dogs were genuine, big hounds eager for a snap at a Christian throat. The third lot of barking came from a man too mean to get a dog licence but who had taken the Percy Edwards course in imitating Dobermann-Pinschers, those dogs that molest felons at a short word from the handler.

So I settle for the private, passive Christmas, sitting quite still, cautiously wishing humanity well and giving thanks for the tireless stream of more or less cogent images proceeding from the set.

My own guess it that the last World War will be fought between the literate and thoughtful and the vandalistic mob. The cause of the war might well be a decision to repeat 'Match of the Day' on all channels right through the week.

*

For those wishing to commit sin, a mining village is the hardest terrain. An extra-mural sinner in that setting is the object of more intense research than atomic energy or the toxic reach of mercury.

The Year That Leaked

Any completed year in this jigging epoch, condensed in recollection, is a cosh of time, and it never fails to connect with the back of my neck with ruthless impact. Normally it will have me reeling until February of the next year. This one now closing will keep me numb until June.

It has been a jittery time. Unemployment, inflation and the organised resentment of their victims pad about like leopards around a frightened Kraal.

Civic solemnity and personal honesty edge a little nearer to the boneyard. Prophets of doom reading the writing on the wall are about the only proof of surviving literacy. These are seemingly two types of age in which values fall disastrously, when money loses its value and when it doesn't.

We man the Alamo for a few pathetic little rearguard actions on behalf of honourable conduct. A handful of peccant councillors and officials, after long trials costing far more than what they misappropriated, are occasionally lodged in gaol and the clanging of prison doors cannot be heard against the din of amiable fiddling that has become our true national anthem. Property rights are regarded with the sort of ironic detachment you would expect from a brotherhood of baboons.

Shoplifting is probably the clearest index of our slap-happy morality. The year has shown boom conditions in this field of enterprise. There are stores in which even the manager has to be nailed to the floor.

A woman not even listed by the police as a notable performer in the lifting line, was found to have a parlour so packed with loot it took two five-ton lorries to take it away.

Another lady in a store was taken to the manager's office in a state of apparent heart collapse, her face bathed in tears. She was found to have a stolen frozen chicken under her hat. The weight and temperature of the bird plus the tension of the moment had caused her to fall apart.

That is defrosting the hard way. The idea of an icy fowl astride the noggin appeals to me. It would be bound in the long run to improve morality. I think that the woman should get at least part of the Carmen Miranda Award for coy headgear.

Miss Miranda, you will remember, in times less sombre than ours, used to wear fruit salads. She'd have looked less blithe under a canopy of cold duck, especially under the hard eye of a store detective.

The only things we guard with real success are the secrets of our shames.

*

Look closely at any man who has made himself absolutely clear and you will see that he has become a little more sinister.

*

I never liked spies.

CY £4.95